# Introduction to Mathematical Structures

# Introduction to Mathematical Structures

CHARLES K. GORDON, Jr.

*Dickenson Publishing Company, Inc.*
*Belmont, California*

Library of Congress Catalog Card No.: 67-24567

Printed in the United States of America

# Preface

This book has been written for students in the biological, social, or behavioral sciences. Our attempt is not so much to develop manipulative skills as it is to encourage the reader to carry over into mathematics the analytical frame of mind he has acquired in his own area of specialization and to introduce him to some new and powerful concepts.

We have sought only to provide an introduction to a number of branches of mathematics, the examination of which will prove rewarding to tne reader. Different readers, of course, will be attracted to different branches and may want to proceed to a more detailed examination of them. This may be accomplished through standard formal course work (such as a one-year course in probability theory, or a one-semester course in matrix algebra, and so on) or through individual study by consulting the References section immediately following the regular text. Hopefully we will have supplied the busy reader with enough material so that he may judge, without having wasted too much time or effort, whether or not the material treated herein might profitably find application in his own area of specialization.

This book has been written to be *read*, rather than meticulously studied, by those readers having more than a passing acquaintance with mathematics. And it is hoped that by our deliberately keeping the organization and style rather informal throughout, the book also will be more palatable to those with little or no prior formal training in mathematics—and perhaps even be fun!

One of the big problems when embarking upon a new field of mathematics is in knowing just how to *apply* the strange new notation and terminology. (It is rather like learning a foreign language in this respect.)

v

For this reason we have developed a small set of carefully prepared exercises at the end of each chapter that have been specifically designed to be thought-provoking and to develop the reader's skill in the kind of reasoning that is peculiar to mathematics. In a number of cases these exercises introduce new, additional concepts which, owing to their specialized nature, were felt not to belong to the text proper. The exercises form an integral part of the text; where time or inclination may dictate that some be skipped, they should at least all be read, since on a number of occasions the discussions in a chapter presuppose familiarity with the material in some preceding exercise. The answers to these exercises, in most cases, have been set down in considerable detail—again to help the reader acquire a feeling for the heuristics of mathematical argument.

It gives me great pleasure to acknowledge the many valuable and detailed suggestions offered by Professor D. G. McTavish of the Sociology Department at California State College at Los Angeles. Some of these, but unfortunately not all, it has been possible to incorporate into this text. Needless to say, any shortcomings that still remain are my own responsibility. I am also grateful to Professor Walter Albrecht of the Mathematics Department at Long Beach State College, who called my attention to a number of errors in the manuscript and who also made a number of useful suggestions.

C. K. G.

*Los Angeles, California*

# Contents

# Introduction to Mathematical Structures

# 1/ Introduction

A set is a *well-defined (unambiguous) collection of distinct elements*. Some examples are:

1. the set of all books in a particular library;
2. the set of neurons involved in a reflex arc;
3. the set of all tasks performed in the manufacturing of some article;
4. the set of symptoms involved in a disease;
5. the set of all fractions between 0 and 1;
6. the set of all U.S. bases on the moon.

These are, clearly, all well-defined "collections" of distinct "elements." (By "distinct" we simply mean that the elements of the set are all different.)

The term "element," rather than "object" or "thing," is preferred in order to be perfectly general and noncommittal about the constituents of a set. The term, as used here, is a *technical term* and, as such, means precisely what *we choose* it to mean. Indeed, since one has to start somewhere (assuming the desirability of excluding circular definitions), "element" will be taken as a *primitive, undefined* term, along with the term "collection." Thus, technically, there is nothing astonishing in the convention that a "collection" may consist of just one element or, even, of no elements (since we have nowhere said what we mean by a "collection")!

Therefore we may speak, sensibly, about the collection of books in John Smith's library even though Smith owns but a single book. This is a set consisting of one, and only one, element. Furthermore, it is important to bear in mind the distinction between a set and the elements composing it,

1

even in this case. Suppose Jones owns three books—$b_1$, $b_2$, $b_3$; then we may symbolize the collection of books in Jones' library by enclosing the elements of the set (or a description of them) in braces, as $\{b_1, b_2, b_3\}$. The distinction between the library and the books constituting it is obvious in this case. We desire to maintain this distinction between, say, $b_5$, a single book owned by Smith, and a single-book library $\{b_5\}$, owned by Smith.

Again, observe that the sixth example, of U.S. moon bases, is also a set—that is a perfectly well-defined collection of elements; it just happens to be empty at the present time (1967). Thus, we may speak of a set even when it "contains" *no* elements. Such sets are called *null* sets and may be symbolized by the special symbol $\mathfrak{E}$ (German script E). If we write $B = \mathfrak{E}$, this means that $B$ does not contain any elements—that is, that $B$ is "the empty set." We say "*the* empty set" rather than "*an* empty set," because it is a simple matter to show that, mathematically, there can be only *one* empty set in the sense that any "other" empty set is identical to it (see Exercise 15, Chapter 2).

It is especially important to note that collections such as "the ten most distinguished men in the world today" or "the five greatest ideas in History" are *not* sets in the mathematical sense, for these collections are not "well-defined." There may be certain borderline cases such as "the set of all tasks performed in the execution of a particular job." This collection of tasks appears, in principle, to be well-defined, though in practice it may prove impossible to prepare a list of *all* the tasks performed in the execution of a particular job, even supposing that a task can be well-defined. Thus, in general, we may say that these sets do not exist mathematically. Unfortunately, the question of the mathematical existence of a set is not always so easily resolved. This problem led to some interesting paradoxes during the first half of this century and necessitated a re-examination of the foundations of mathematics.* For our purposes, we will say a collection is "well-defined" only if it is always possible to decide, given any element, whether or not it belongs to the collection (see discussion below).

A set may be characterized, or defined, in either of two ways:

1. by *extension* or enumeration (that is, listing each element by name);
2. by *intension* (not intention!) or description (that is, stating a "property" that the elements "share in common" and that "binds them together" in the collection).

Thus, in the first example given in the opening paragraph, the books can be listed or enumerated, and one might refer to the set:

> {*Interpretation of Dreams, Psychopathology of Everyday Life*, . . . , *The History of an Illusion*}.

---

* See, for example, Reference 7. There is also a fine discussion, in Chapter III, of Reference 13.

Braces, rather than parentheses or brackets, are used to signify a set; the three dots within the braces (or wherever else they appear in the sequel) are to be read "and so on." Notice that the order in which the elements appear in the set is not significant. When it is desired to speak of an *ordered set* it is customary to use parentheses rather than braces. Ordered sets will be discussed later in more detail.

Alternatively, the set in the first example might simply be described by intension in such terms as "the collection of Freud's published technical writings." Notice that "the collection of Freud's writings" is a *different* set. It consists not only of Freud's books and journal articles but also his correspondence and anything else he may have written, published or not. The collection of published technical writings is a subset of the collection of writings. But more of this in a moment. At this point we wish to emphasize merely that one has to be *cautious* and *precise* in defining a set by intension.

Consider the set of books in Jones' library; it might consist of the set:

$$\{The\ Anatomy\ of\ Melancholy,\ Malleus\ Maleficarum,\ Petronius\}.$$

An element's (book's) eligibility for "membership" in this set (library) is determined by whether or not it has a certain property, namely, that of "belonging to Jones' library." The fact that some element, $x$, *belongs to\** a set, $S$, is symbolized

$$x \in S.$$

This expression may be read simply "$x$ in $S$." The individual "entities" constituting the collection are called *members* or *elements* of the set. The relation of an element to a set is that of membership. The inverse relation of a set to an element is that of possession: a set has or has not as a member some particular entity. That is, an entity $x$ is either a member of (or "in") a set $S$ (symbolized as above) or it is not, symbolized

$$x \notin S.$$

The notions of *element, collection,* and *membership* are taken as primitive (undefined): all else may ultimately be defined in terms of these. It is important to realize that the "elements" of a set may themselves be sets, so that we may speak of a set of sets. This is not so surprising. But what is surprising is the fact that, for mathematical purposes, no elements other than sets (and, of course, sets of sets, and so on) need ever be considered [3].†

A relatively small and finite set is usually best defined by explicitly exhibiting the elements making it up, as above. This is particularly true when the elements of a set have nothing much in common aside from the fact that they just happen to have been lumped together under the same

---

* Some alternative renderings are: *is a member of, is an element of,* or *is in.*

† Bracketed numbers refer to References for Additional Reading on page 130.

collection. However, a set such as "the set of all living people who have Ph.D.'s in psychology" is probably best defined intensionally in some such terms as, "the set of all those elements $x$ such that $x$ is a living person and $x$ has a Ph.D. in psychology". This is symbolized

$$S = \{x \mid x \text{ is living person and } x \text{ has a Ph.D. in psychology}\},$$

where the vertical bar between the two $x$'s may be rendered, "such that." Furthermore, certain sets containing infinitely many elements obviously can *only* be defined precisely by intension—that is, by stating some property the elements share in common, as for example:

$$\{x \mid x \text{ is exactly divisible by two}\}$$

is the set of all even numbers. Incidentally, notice that the set of all even prime numbers* can be defined extensionally; it is simply: $\{2\}$. Notice that every set definable in extension can be defined in intension (though the phrasing may appear awkward).

The examples so far serve to introduce some important notions about sets. Thus, a set enjoys certain properties not possessed by its elements, and vice versa. For example, while an entire library may be quite expensive, any individual book (element) need not be. Furthermore, there are certain properties of certain sets that the elements simply can *not* have. Thus, the library (set) might be numerous (that is "large"), while this could not be said of any individual book (element). Conversely, in the penultimate example above, while each number is exactly divisible by two, the set is certainly not exactly divisible by two. And in the last example above, while 2 is an even prime number, $\{2\}$ is not; furthermore, it is not a number of any kind! This clearly brings out the distinction between set $\{2\}$ and its single *member* 2.

In summary, we have seen that a "collection," as technically conceived here, is an entity, or better a *concept*, quite distinct from the "elements" comprising it. Furthermore, the *convention* is adopted of continuing to use this name when the "collection" contains just a single element or even when it contains no elements. We do this because it will turn out to be a useful convention in later developments. When the set under discussion contains no elements, it is said to be *empty*; it is called the *null set* and is symbolized by $\mathfrak{E}$ (German script E); in your writing you may symbolize it by $\varnothing$. Since much nonsense has been written about the "existence" of the null set—or of sets in general, for that matter, mostly by some professional philosophers—we point out once again that for our purposes the question of the (mathematical) existence of a set is resolved once an unequivocal rule is available that allows one to say, for any element, whether it belongs to the set, or not. If all the books have been removed from a library, for example, it is still *appropriate*

---

* A prime number is a positive integer that is (exactly) divisible *only* by itself and by 1; for example, 1, 2, 3, 5, 7, 11, 13, 17, . . . are the first eight primes.

to speak of "the library." The library (set) does not simply cease to exist merely because it contains no books (elements)! To put it another way, we are dealing here with matters of *linguistic convention*. As mentioned previously, the word *collection* is a *technical* term; it has, moreover, the status of a *primitive, undefined* term. We are thus at liberty to use it in such a way that a "collection" having no elements (or just one element) will still be spoken of as a *collection*. One further point of importance may be gathered from the examples so far, and that is that the order in which the elements are listed within the braces is immaterial, as mentioned before.

Incidentally, a word about the usage of "all." This word is ordinarily taken to be synonymous with the expression "each and every." That is, the expression "all of the set . . ." means "each and every *member* of the set . . ." (notice the reference to members here). Thus, "all" is customarily used *distributively*. If, however, one wishes to use the term "all" *collectively*, in order to mention a property of the set not possessed by its elements, the context should make this clear. In the case of finite sets, one may obviously speak either way, depending on one's purpose. In the case of "infinite" sets (for example, "the set of all even numbers"), the situation is by no means so clear-cut. There are those who maintain that the conception of a set as a completed whole, a single *de facto* totality, when the number of elements is "infinite" is inapposite. But this may be no more than a statement of their own views regarding linguistic conventions or the process of conceptualization. The question is: Can one define the set of all even numbers by extension? Of course, one can write $\{2, 4, 6, \ldots\}$—where the three dots stand for "and so on"—but what is the status of the three dots?

In conclusion, the important notions to carry away from this chapter are:

1. A set is a "collection" of "elements."

2. The "collection" may be empty, contain just a single element, or contain more than one element.

3. The order of the elements constituting the collection is inconsequential; that is to say, we do not distinguish between the collections $\{b_1, b_2, b_3\}$, $\{b_2, b_3, b_1\}$, $\{b_2, b_1, b_3\}$; if these are collections of books, for example, they obviously all represent the same collection.

4. The elements in the collection are all *distinct*; that is, the set $\{a, b, a, c, b\}$ is written simply as $\{a, b, c\}$—strictly speaking, the former is not really a *set*.

Finally, since we have nowhere said what an "element" is, there is nothing to prevent an element from itself being a set, and we may speak of a set (or a "collection") $\mathscr{C}$ of sets, say:

$$\mathscr{C} = \{A, B, C, D\},$$

where $A$, $B$, $C$, and $D$—the "elements" of $\mathscr{C}$—are sets. Thus, the United States is a set of states, but each state, in turn, may be regarded as a set of counties.

# EXERCISES

1. If a coin is tossed twice in a row, we may exhibit the set of all possibilities as follows: {HT, HH, TH, TT}. What is the set of possibilities when a coin is tossed three times in a row?

2. Examine your result above to write the sets showing all cases in which:
   (a) At least two tails may result.
   (b) At least three heads may result.
   (c) Two heads in a row may result.
   (d) No tails result.
   (e) At most two tails result. (*Caution:* This says only that the *most* number of tails may not exceed two; it says nothing about the *least* number of tails.)
   (f) At least two heads and at most two heads result.
   (g) At most two heads in a row result.
   (h) At most two heads in a row and no tails result.
   (i) At most two heads and three tails result.
   (j) An even number of heads and an even number of tails result.

3. (a) Define the set {1, 3, 5, 7, 9, 11, . . .} by intension.
   (b) Define the set $\{x \mid x$ is a prime number$\}$ by extension (that is, enumerating some of its members).
   (c) Define the set $\{x \mid x$ is an even positive integer$\}$ by extension.
   (d) Write the set (extension) whose elements are the odd prime numbers.
   (e) Give the set (extension) of all even prime numbers.
   (f) Define $\{x \mid x$ is a positive integer divisible by 3$\}$ by extension.
   (g) Define {5, 10, 15, 20, 25, 30, 35, . . .} by intension.
   (h) Define {6, 12, 18, 24, 30, 36, . . .} by intension.
   (i) Define $\{x \mid x$ is a result obtained when three coins are tossed simultaneously$\}$ by extension.

4. Which of the following statements are true and which are false?
   (a) $9 \in \{x \mid x$ is a prime number$\}$.
   (b) Los Angeles $\in$ {The United States of America}.
   (c) Hawaii $\in \{x \mid x$ is an American city).
   (d) $0 \in \mathfrak{E}$.
   (e) $\frac{1}{2} \in \{x \mid x$ is a small number$\}$.
   (f) $\{\frac{1}{2}, \frac{1}{3}\} \in \{x \mid x$ is a fraction$\}$.

5. Convert the following statements to set notation.
   (a) 2 is not an odd number.
   (b) The null set contains no members.
   (c) The set of all unicorns is empty (Symbolize "is" by using the equal sign, $=$).
   (d) {1, 2} is an element of the set containing the following three elements: {1, 2}, {2, 3}, and {3, 4}.

(e) The collection of all pairs of positive fractions whose numerators are 1 and whose denominators differ by 1 (such as $\frac{1}{2}$ and $\frac{1}{3}$) is equal to C.

(f) $\{\frac{1}{25}, \frac{1}{26}\}$ belongs to the set defined in (e) above.

(g) $\{\frac{1}{25}, \frac{1}{27}\}$ does not belong to the set defined in (e) above.

6. Would you say that a set can contain itself as a member? What about the set of all concepts? Is not this itself a concept and does it not therefore also belong to the set of all concepts?

7. Can you think of a major distinction to be drawn between the set $\{x \mid x$ is a unicorn$\}$ and the elements belonging to the set?

8. Write down a list of sets from your own field of specialization. Can you think of collections that are not well-defined in your field and find reasons why? Can you think of ways to get around this?

9. Presumably, the set of all life-forms can be characterized by extension (though what a job that would be). To see whether something is a life-form we would merely look at the things in our collection (set), one by one, to see if it appears there. Yet why is it claimed that there is no satisfactory definition of "life"?

10. Can you characterize the set of all life-forms by intension?

11. At one time, organic compounds (such as sugar) were distinguished from inorganic compounds (such as salt) by the fact that the former were derived from living, or once-living, matter (such as sugar cane or beets). Could one sensibly speak of the set of organic compounds in those days? (Hint: What is the set of living or once-living matter from which they are derived?)

12. Can one sensibly speak of the set of organic compounds today? Can the chemist decide, for any pure compound presented to him, whether it belongs to the set of organic or inorganic compounds?

13. Can the biologist (or microbiologist) always decide whether a substance presented to him is living (or once-living)?

# 2/ Sets, Subsets, and Set Inclusion

Usually, one begins a discussion by picking out a certain, often fairly large, collection of elements for study—for example, the set of all points on a line or in a plane. This collection may be regarded as the universe of discourse, and the corresponding set is called the *universal set* or, simply, the *universe*. We will symbolize it by $\mathfrak{U}$ (German script U). For example, in one study, the universe might be the set of all animals at some particular zoo. Thus we might write

$$\mathfrak{U} = \{a_1, a_2, \ldots, a_n\},$$

where the $a_i$ represent animals and there are $n$ of them. The set $R$, of reptiles considered alone, is said to be a *subset* of $\mathfrak{U}$. This relation between sets is symbolized:

$$R \subseteq \mathfrak{U},$$

which may be rendered as "$R$ is a subset of $\mathfrak{U}$," or as "$R$ is included in $\mathfrak{U}$." In general, given any two sets $A$ and $B$, we shall say that $A$ is a *subset* of $B$, symbolized $A \subseteq B$, provided that every element $x \in A$ (read: "$x$ in $A$") is also an element in $B$. If, in addition, there is at least one element in $B$ that is not an element of $A$, then $A$ is said to be a *proper subset* of $B$, symbolized:

$$A \subset B.$$

In the finite case, the reader may think of the set $B$ as being "larger" than $A$, though we have not introduced (and, indeed, will not introduce here) the sophisticated notion of the "size" of a set—a notion requiring careful definition, particularly in the case of sets containing infinitely many elements. In this latter case a *proper* subset may obtain as many elements as the universe of which it is a subset. (This will be discussed further in Section 3.1.)

As another example, let

$$M_1 = \{x \mid x \text{ is a mammal}\}$$

and

$$M_2 = \{x \mid x \text{ suckles its young}\};$$

then

$$M_2 \subseteq M_1.$$

This symbolism also permits us to adopt the useful convention that every set is ("improperly") included in itself, symbolized

$$A \subseteq A, \qquad \text{for any set } A.$$

For this reason "$\subseteq$" is said to be a *reflexive* relation (see Section 4.3.1). Another example of an obviously reflexive relation is that of identity, since everything is identical to itself; for example, every set is identical to itself. This is probably a good place to define the notion of identity between sets.

Two sets, $A$ and $B$, will be said to be *identical*, or *equal*, ($A = B$) if, and only if, every element in $A$ is an element in $B$ *and vice versa*. Thus, if when $x \in A$ *then* $x \in B$, *and* when $x \in B$, *then* $x \in A$, we will say that $A = B$.

The notion of the identity of two sets must be carefully distinguished from the related notion of "equivalence" of sets. For the time being we can be satisfied with the following informal discussion. The sets $A$ and $B$ are said to be *equivalent* to each other, symbolized $A \sim B$, if, and only if, their elements can be exhaustively paired with each other. Thus, for example,

$$\{a, b, c\} \sim \{x, y, z\} \sim \{3, 1, 2\}.$$

This should be contrasted with the case of equality—for example,

$$\{a, b, c\} = \{b, c, a\} = \{c, a, b\} = \{b, c, a, b\}.$$

We shall have more to say about equivalence later on (Section 4.3.4).

The symbol $\in$ introduced earlier should be carefully distinguished from the symbol $\subseteq$. Notice that the latter is defined in terms of the former. Furthermore, $\subseteq$ is *always* reflexive, whereas $\in$ customarily is *not*. Also, $\subseteq$ is transitive (see below), but $\in$ is not. Confusion is most likely to occur in cases wherein the elements themselves are sets. This may readily be avoided by some such artifice as the use of italicized, boldface, or script letters for collections (sets) of sets. Thus, if $\mathfrak{A}$ (German script A) is a collection whose elements happen to be *sets*, then

$$B \in \mathfrak{A}$$

says that $B$ is *one* of the *sets* in the collection $\mathfrak{A}$, while

$$\mathfrak{B} \subseteq \mathfrak{A}$$

says that $\mathfrak{B}$ (German script B) is a subcollection (subset) of the collection (set of sets) $\mathfrak{A}$. For example, if $\mathfrak{A} = \{A, B, C, D\}$, where $A$, $B$, $C$, and $D$ are sets, then, for example,

$$B \in \mathfrak{A},$$

and if $\mathfrak{B} = \{A, D\}$, say, then

$$\mathfrak{B} \subseteq \mathfrak{A}.$$

Indeed,

$$\mathfrak{B} \subset \mathfrak{A}.$$

Again, if $A = \{a\}$, then

$$a \in A$$

but

$$\{a\} \subseteq A$$

(since every element in the set on the left, in the last example, is a member of the set on the right), where again we emphasize the distinction between $\{a\}$ and $a$.*

In the example of the zoo, above, the set $R$, of reptiles, may be considered as a collection of sets, namely, the set of snakes, $S$, the set of lizards, $L$, and so on. Thus, when $R$ is so conceived, we would write:

$$S \in \mathfrak{R}$$

and

$$L \in \mathfrak{R}$$

and so on. On the other hand, if $R$ is conceived as a collection of individual reptiles—that is, each individual, particular reptile (by name, if you wish) in the zoo—then the set of all snakes from that collection of reptiles is a subset of $R$:

$$S \subset R;$$

if the *only* reptiles this zoo had were snakes, we would write, instead:

$$S \subseteq R;$$

indeed,

$$S = R.$$

Notice, furthermore, that from the fact that $R \subseteq \mathfrak{U}$ and $S \subseteq R$ we conclude that $S \subseteq \mathfrak{U}$. It is for this reason that the relation of inclusion (both $\subseteq$ and $\subset$) is said to be *transitive* (as may readily be proven). It will always be the case that the subset of a subset of a given set is also a subset of the given set. But an element of an element of a given set is not necessarily an element of the given set—that is, $\in$ is not necessarily transitive.

---

* This distinction perhaps becomes transparent in the case of the following inequality:

$$\{\{a, b\}\} \neq \{a, b\},$$

where the left side is a set containing one member, namely, $\{a, b\}$, while the right side is a set containing two members, $a$ and $b$. Notice that the set on the left contains an "element" that is itself a set.

As another example of a transitive relation, consider "is the ancestor of." Evidently, the ancestor of an ancestor is also an ancestor. Notice, however, that the relation "is the father of" is *not* transitive; for if $A$ is the father of $B$ and $B$ is the father of $C$ then $A$ is most certainly *not* the *father* of $C$. Such a relation is said to be *intransitive*. The relation "is a relative of" is *sometimes* transitive and is said to be *mesotransitive*. Thus, a relation may be not transitive either because it is intransitive or because it is mesotransitive. Relations in general will be discussed further in Chapter 4.

To see that $\in$ need not necessarily be transitive consider:

$$S = \{\{a, b\}, \{c, d, e\}\}.$$

Then

$$a \in \{a, b\}$$

and

$$\{a, b\} \in S,$$

but

$$a \notin S.$$

Incidentally, we can now mention one of the difficulties hinted at previously as regards the mathematical existence of sets. *Prima facie*, the notion of "the set of all sets" appears at least *conceptually* feasible. Let us call this set $\mathscr{A}$; thus,

$$\mathscr{A} = \{A, B, C, \ldots\}.$$

Unfortunately, $\mathscr{A}$ is not the set of *all* sets, for $\mathscr{A}$ itself is missing from the collection inside the braces. In an attempt to remedy this situation we write:

$$\mathscr{A} = \{\mathscr{A}, A, B, C, \ldots\}.$$

But again, we see here that we do not have the collection of *all* sets, for $\mathscr{A}$ itself is missing from the collection. And so on.

In Chapter 1 we discussed two general ways of forming sets: by description and by enumeration. We now see a third means of generating sets: by forming the various subsets of a given set.

Given any set $S$, we can describe the number of distinct subsets that may be formed from it. Suppose $S = \{a, b, c\}$, a set with three elements; some of the subsets of $S$ are

$$\{a\}, \quad \{b\}, \quad \{c\}, \quad \{a, b\}, \quad \{a, c\}, \quad \{b, c\}, \quad \{a, b, c\}.$$

Notice that every element belonging to, say, the set $\{a\}$ (there happens to be only one such element) is also an element of $S$. Furthermore, since order is immaterial, we do not distinguish between sets $\{a, b\}$ and $\{b, a\}$—these are one and the same set. Clearly, $\{a, b, c\}$ is a subset of $S$ (it happens to be an improper subset), since every element in $\{a, b, c\}$ also belongs to $S$. As already pointed out, every set, $S$, is considered to be a subset of itself— another one of those linguistic conventions alluded to earlier.

Additionally, it turns out to be convenient to consider the empty set as being a subset of every set. This convention is not at variance with the definition of a subset. For *if* $x \in \mathfrak{E}$ (it happens not to be), then $x \in S$; the definition (of subset) is said to be satisfied *vacuously*. Perhaps an easier way of showing this is the following. Suppose $\mathfrak{E}$ were *not* a subset of $S$. This could only happen if $\mathfrak{E}$ contained some element not in $S$. But this is impossible since $\mathfrak{E}$ is empty. Therefore, $\mathfrak{E}$ must be a subset of $S$. With this understanding, the set of *all* subsets of $S$ is

$$\{\{a\}, \{b\}, \{c\}, \{a, b\}, \{a, c\}, \{b, c\}, S, \mathfrak{E}\}.$$

Observe that $2^3 = 8$ subsets may be formed from a set $S$ of 3 elements—that is, the set above contains 8 elements. In general, given a set $S$ of $n$ elements, there are $2^n$ subsets that can be formed from $S$. This result is, after all, fairly obvious. Suppose one is thinking of constructing some subset of $S$. For each one of the $n$ elements in $S$, one has the choice of including it in this subset or not. Since there are two such choices for each one of these $n$ elements, there are altogether $2 \times 2 \times 2 \times \cdots \times n$ times, or $2^n$ subsets. This is one reason why it is convenient to agree that every set is a subset of itself and that the null set is a subset of every set.

The number of different subsets *of m elements* of a set of $n$ elements (where $m < n$) is not found so quickly. However, this turns out to be simply the case of finding the number of combinations of $n$ things taken $m$ at a time, for which we have the formula from elementary algebra:

$$C(n, m) = \frac{n!}{m!\,(n-m)!},$$

where $n!$ (and $m!$) is defined as the product of the positive integers from 1 through $n$:

$$n! = 1 \times 2 \times 3 \times \cdots \times (n-1) \times n.$$

(We define $0! = 1$).* In the present case, for example, the number of different subsets of $S$ containing exactly 2 elements is

$$C(3, 2) = \frac{3!}{2!\,(3-2)!} = \frac{1 \cdot 2 \cdot 3}{1 \cdot 2 \cdot 1} = 3.$$

Again, the number of subsets of a set with 4 elements is $2^4 = 16$ while, for example, the number of subsets containing exactly 2 elements is

$$C(4, 2) = \frac{4!}{2!\,(4-2)!} = \frac{4!}{2!\,2!} = \frac{3 \cdot 4}{2!} = 6$$

---

* That this definition is reasonable can be seen as follows. Evidently, $n! = (n-1)!\,n$, or $(n-1)! = n!/n$; now, let $n = 1$.

and the number containing exactly 3 elements is

$$C(4, 3) = \frac{4!}{3!\,1!} = 4.$$

We have now an additional scheme for generating new sets. The set of *all* subsets of a given set $A$, sometimes symbolized $2^A$ (for obvious reasons), is called the *power set* of $A$. The "elements" of the power set of $A$ are *sets*, $X$, such that each set is a subset of $A$. As a simple example, suppose $A = \{a\}$, then $2^A = \{\mathfrak{E}, \{a\}\}$ contains $2^1 = 2$ elements. Notice that $\{\{a\}\}$ is a subset of $2^A$. This set, containing the single "element" $\{a\}$, is useful for once again emphasizing the difference between $\subseteq$ and $\in$. Notice that

$$\{a\} \in \{\{a\}\}$$

but

$$\{a\} \nsubseteq \{\{a\}\} \qquad \text{(read } \nsubseteq \text{ as "is not included in")}$$

for the set on the left contains $a$ while the set on the right contains $\{a\}$. Incidentally, from all that has been said regarding $\in$ and $\subseteq$, the reader should not conclude that an element of a given set cannot also be a subset of that set. Thus,

$$\mathfrak{E} \in \{\mathfrak{E}\}$$

but, also,

$$\mathfrak{E} \subseteq \{\mathfrak{E}\}.$$

Notice that $\{\mathfrak{E}\}$ is an example of a nonempty set ($\mathfrak{E}$ is empty; but $\{\mathfrak{E}\}$ is not!) *all* of whose elements are subsets of that set.

We will adopt the notation

$$P^A = \{X \mid X \subseteq A\}$$

for the power set of $A$. This may be read, "the set of all sets $X$ such that $X \subseteq A$." Power sets have a number of interesting properties which will be developed in the exercises.

As an aid in visualizing relations among sets, the sets may be "pictured" by areas inside closed curves of arbitrary size and shape within a region fixed as the universe $\mathfrak{U}$. For example, a glance at Figure 1(a) is sufficient to convince one that the elements of every set in $\mathfrak{U}$, such as $A$, also belong to $\mathfrak{U}$. Since each and every element $x \in A$, is also (automatically) an element $x \in \mathfrak{U}$, we see graphically what it means to say $A$ is a subset of $\mathfrak{U}$.

As we have shown it here, $A$ happens to be a proper subset of $\mathfrak{U}$ since there is at least one element $y \in \mathfrak{U}$ such that $y \notin A$. We see that these latter elements afford here a fourth means of defining (constructing) sets. The set of all elements that do *not* belong to $A$, which may be expressed $\{y \mid y \notin A\}$ and in words as "the set of all elements $y$ such that $y$ is not a member of $A$," is said to form (or lie in) the *relative complement* of $A$ or in the complement of $A$ relative to $\mathfrak{U}$, symbolized $\mathfrak{U} - A$.

Thus

$$\mathfrak{U} - A = \{y \mid y \notin A\}.$$

Pictorially (Figure 1(b)), $\mathfrak{U} - A$ corresponds to all the "area" outside of the set $A$.

When the relative complement of a set $A$ is taken with respect to the universe, $\mathfrak{U} - A$, it is customary to speak simply of the *complement of A*, symbolized $\bar{A}$ (or sometimes, $A'$). It is to be emphasized, however, that the universe must be known. That is to say, "the set of all elements not in $A$" is not well-defined (and hence not really a set) until the universe is specified.

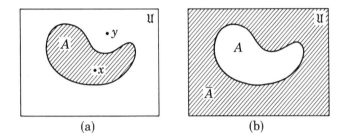

(a)                              (b)

**Figure 1.** (a) The set $A$ (shaded). (b) The set $\bar{A}$ (shaded).

Thus, if $A$ is the set of all points on a line between 0 and 1, $\bar{A}$ could be the set of all points on the line outside this interval, or the set of all points in the plane (or in space) not on the line, or, for that matter, the set of all unicorns, for a unicorn is also not a point on a line between 0 and 1.

In summary, we say $A$ is a *subset* of $B$, symbolized $A \subseteq B$, whenever every element in $A$ is also an element in $B$. If, in addition, $B$ contains at least one element that is not in $A$, $A$ is said to be a *proper subset* of $B$, symbolized $A \subset B$. Often the adjective "proper" is omitted, the symbol $\subset$ showing what is meant. Whenever we have $A \subset B$ we must, of course, have $A \subseteq B$ as well; the converse is obviously not true. But this does *not* mean that $A \subseteq B$ *precludes* the possibility of $A \subset B$. The expression $A \subseteq B$ is often used simply because it is desired to leave open the question of whether or not $A \subset B$.

Two sets are said to be *identical*, or *equal*, symbolized $A = B$, whenever every element in $A$ is an element in $B$, and vice versa. Thus, if you can establish that $A \subseteq B$ *and* that $B \subseteq A$, you may conclude that $A = B$.

Two sets are said to be *equivalent* when their elements can be paired exhaustively with each other. For example, the set of all odd numbers is equivalent to the set of all even numbers. The sets are often said to have the same *power* when this is the case.

Set inclusion has the following properties

1. (a) If $A \subseteq B$ and $B \subseteq C$, then $A \subseteq C$.
   (b) If $A \subset B$ and $B \subset C$, then $A \subset C$. } (Transitivity)

2. For any set $A$, $A \subseteq A$.  (Reflexivity)

3. For any set $A$, $\mathfrak{E} \subseteq A$; in fact. $\mathfrak{E} \subset A$.

Given a set with $n$ elements, the total number of possible subsets of this set is given by $2^n$. The total number of different subsets containing exactly $m$ elements (where $m \leq n$) is given by the formula for finding the number of combinations of $n$ things taken $m$ at a time:

$$C(n, m) = \frac{n!}{m! \, (n - m)!},$$

where $n!$ is defined by

$$n! = 1 \times 2 \times 3 \times \cdots \times (n - 1) \times n$$

and

$$0! = 1$$

by definition.

Given a set $A$, the *power set of $A$*, symbolized $P^A$ (or sometimes $2^A$), is the collection (set) of all subsets of $A$. Thus, $P^A$ is a set whose elements are themselves sets.

The *complement of $A$ relative to $\mathfrak{U}$*, symbolized $\mathfrak{U} - A$, consists of all elements in $\mathfrak{U}$ that are not in $A$:

$$\mathfrak{U} - A = \{x \mid x \in \mathfrak{U} \quad \text{and} \quad x \notin A\}.$$

In particular, $\mathfrak{U} - A$ is usually simply spoken of as the *complement of $A$*, symbolized $\bar{A}$ (or sometimes $A'$).

## EXERCISES

1. List the set of all subsets of $S = \{\text{HT, HH, TH, TT}\}$. Recall that there will be $2^4 = 16$ of these, including $\mathfrak{E}$ and $S$ itself.

2. Which of the following statements are true and which are false?
   (a) Los Angeles $\subseteq$ {The United States of America}.
   (b) Los Angeles $\subseteq \{x \mid x$ is one of our fifty States$\}$.
   (c) $2 \subseteq \{x \mid x$ is an even number$\}$.
   (d) $\{x \mid x$ is an odd positive integer$\} \subseteq \{x \mid x$ is a positive integer$\}$.
   (e) $\{x \mid x$ is an odd positive integer$\} \subset \{x \mid x$ is a positive integer$\}$.
   (f) $\{x \mid x$ is an odd positive integer$\} = \{x \mid x$ is not (exactly) divisible by 2$\}$.
   (g) $\{x \mid x$ is an odd positive integer$\} \subseteq \{x \mid x$ is not (exactly) divisible by 2$\}$.
   (h) $\{x \mid x$ is an odd positive integer$\} \subset \{x \mid x$ is not (exactly) divisible by 2$\}$.
   (i) $\{x \mid x$ is an odd positive integer$\} \sim \{x \mid x$ is an odd negative integer$\}$.

3. In how many ways can one pick three experimental subjects from among five without regard for order? In other words, how many 3-element subsets can one form from $\{a, b, c, d, e\}$? Notice that we do not distinguish between, say, $\{a, b, c\}$ and $\{b, c, a\}$—these are considered to be one and the same subset of $\{a, b, c, d, e\}$.

4. In how many different orders can one perform five tasks? (Hint: Suppose there are five spaces to be filled with five letters $a$, $b$, $c$, $d$, and $e$: $-----$; how many choices do we have for the first space? Once having made a choice from among the five letters, how many choices are there left for the second space? Having made this choice, in how many ways may the third space be filled? And so on.) Each arrangement is called a *permutation*. In general, how many permutations are there on $n$ things?

5. In how many different ways can one assign 5 experimental subjects to 3 different groups? (Hint: In how many different ways can one fill 3 spaces, $---$, from among 5 letters: $a$, $b$, $c$, $d$ and $e$?). Compare with your answer to Exercise 3 above.

6. In how many ways can $m$ spaces be filled from among $n$ different things? Can you derive a formula for this?

7. List the 3-element subsets of $\{a, b, c, d\}$. How many different arrangements are there on the elements in each of these subsets? Is the total of these equal to the number of different arrangements in which you can fill three spaces, $---$, from among four letters: $a$, $b$, $c$, $d$?

8. Can you derive a formula that will give the number of $m$-element subsets that can be formed from an $n$-element set? (Hint: How are the permutations related to the combinations?)

9. (a) If $A = \{a, b\}$, then $P^A = ?$
   (b) Is $\{a, b\} \subseteq P^A$?
   (c) Is $\{a, b\} \in P^A$?
   (d) Is $\{\{a, b\}\} \subseteq P^A$?

10. (a) What is $P^{\mathfrak{E}}$?
    (b) What is $P^{P^{\mathfrak{E}}}$? (Hint: This asks for the power set of $\{\mathfrak{E}\}$).
    (c) Does $P^{\mathfrak{E}}$ differ from $P^{\{\mathfrak{E}\}}$?
    (d) What is the next power set in the family or sequence $P^{\mathfrak{E}}$, $P^{\{\mathfrak{E}\}}$, . . .?
    (e) How are these power sets related?

11. Convince yourself that $\mathfrak{E} \in P^A$ and $A \in P^A$. (Notice that it is *not* true, in general, that $\mathfrak{E} \in A$ for any arbitrary set; what we *have* said previously is that $\mathfrak{E} \subseteq A$ for any arbitrary set.)

12. Show that
    (a) $P^A \subseteq P^B$ if, and only if,* $A \subseteq B$.
    (b) $\{x\} \in P^A$ if, and only if, $x \in A$.
    (c) $B \in P^A$ if, and only if, $B \subseteq A$.
    (d) $P^{\{a\}} = \{\mathfrak{E}, \{a\}\}$.

---

* When the mathematician says that $P$ is true if and only if $Q$ is true, he means: if $P$ is true then $Q$ is true *and* if $Q$ is true then $P$ is true.

13.  (a)  $\bar{\mathfrak{E}} = ?$
     (b)  $\bar{\mathfrak{U}} = ?$

14.  State whether each of the following is true or false:
     (a)  $\mathfrak{U} - A \subseteq A$?
     (b)  $\mathfrak{U} - A \subseteq \mathfrak{U}$?
     (c)  $\mathfrak{E} \subseteq \bar{\mathfrak{U}}$?
     (d)  $\mathfrak{U} \subseteq \bar{\mathfrak{E}}$?

15.  Prove that $\mathfrak{E}$ is unique. (Hint: Assume there's a null set $\mathfrak{E}'$ such that $\mathfrak{E}' \neq \mathfrak{E}$ and show that this leads to a contradiction.)

16.  Prove that if $A \subseteq B$, then $\bar{B} \subseteq \bar{A}$.

17.  Prove that $A = B$ if, and only if, both $A \subseteq B$ and $B \subseteq A$.

18.  Prove that if $\{\{a\}, \{a, b\}\} = \{\{c\}, \{c, d\}\}$ then both $a = c$ and $b = d$. Notice that the *converse* of this statement is trivial: obviously, if $a = c$ and $b = d$ then $\{\{a\}, \{a, b\}\} = \{\{c\}, \{c, d\}\}$. Thus, your proof really establishes that $\{\{a\}, \{a, b\}\} = \{\{c\}, \{c, d\}$ if and only if both $a = c$ and $b = d$.

19.  Can a set have a proper subset containing an element that the set itself contains?

20.  May a *subset* of a given set also be an *element* of that set?

# 3/ Operations on Sets

## 3.1 Set Union

Obviously the two sets $A$ and $\bar{A}$, considered at the end of the last chapter, together make up the entire universe $\mathfrak{U}$. One might, therefore, be tempted to write:
$$A + \bar{A} = \mathfrak{U}.$$
On deliberation, however, one will realize that the "equation" above does not mean exactly the same thing as it does in arithmetic or algebra.

What does it mean to "add" two sets? We might be tempted to regard the relation above (we cannot accurately call it an *equation*) as a symbolic way of stating that when all the "area" $A$ is "added" to the "area" $\bar{A}$, the total "area" $\mathfrak{U}$ results (Figure 1(b)). But, after all, these areas are no more than a visual aid and are of no consequence as far as the formal development of set theory is concerned. Furthermore, matters are not improved if we seek to interpret the addition of two sets as signifying, simply, the addition of the "numbers" of their elements. For what does it mean to "add" the infinitely many points enclosed by the area $A$ to the infinitely many points in $\bar{A}$? In other words, such an interpretation of "addition" is meaningless in those cases in which the sets to be added contain infinitely many elements.

As we will see, there is a sense in which the set of all integers may be regarded as the (set-theoretic) "sum" of the even and odd integers. But, obviously, one cannot simply "add," in the ordinary sense, the ("infinite") number of all* odd numbers to the ("infinite") number of all even numbers.

---

* The distinction between the two senses in which the word "all" may be used is found again. In most mathematical circles it is considered legitimate to use "all" in the collective sense here. But apparently the controversy remains unsettled.

Indeed, the set containing both odd and even numbers is no "larger," in the sense of *not* containing any "more" elements, than the set containing only even (or only odd) numbers.* This result certainly does violence to our common-sense ("common" meaning "commonplace") notion of "addition." Here, when we "add" the set of all odd integers to the set of all even integers we have not increased the "size" of the set; it still contains the same "number" of elements.

These considerations point up the fact that, as far as sets are concerned, we cannot speak of "addition" in the conventional (arithmetic) sense. Nor should we wish to. Set theory is not arithmetic and sets are not simply numbers. Adding a pair of numbers is a perfectly well-defined *arithmetical* operation, but adding a pair of sets is not defined.

It is possible, however, to define an operation between sets that, in some respects, is analogous to the operation of addition between two numbers. This is the operation of *union* between sets, symbolized "$\cup$". Thus, we write

$$A \cup \bar{A} = \mathfrak{U}.$$

In words, "the union of a set with its complement is the universe."

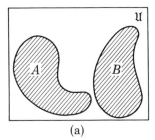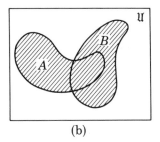

(a)                    (b)

**Figure 2.** The set $A \cup B$ (shaded). (a) Nonoverlapping
sets. (b) Overlapping sets.

The union of two sets, $A \cup B$, is defined as that *set* all of whose elements are either in $A$ or in $B$ (or both). Symbolically,

$$S = A \cup B = \{x \mid x \in A \text{ or } x \in B\},$$

where the "or" is to be interpreted as the inclusive "or" (that is, "either or both"). Graphically, the union of two sets may be pictured as in Figure 2. Sets $A$ and $B$ are illustrated in Figure 2(a) as having no elements in common,

---

* This is quite readily seen by comparing these two sets, element for element, as shown below:

$$N = \{1, 2, 3, 4, 5, \ldots\},$$
$$E = \{2, 4, 6, 8, 10, \ldots\}.$$

It is seen that to every element in the "larger" set of even-and-odd numbers there is a corresponding element (namely, its double) in the set $E$ of all even numbers alone. Furthermore, this is a "one-to-one" correspondence, which works both ways, so that, in fact, the two sets are exhausted by such pairing. One-to-one correspondences are discussed further in Section 4.5.

and in Figure 2(b) as "sharing" those elements represented by the overlap of the two areas. The significance of overlap is developed in Section 3.2 below.

As an example, suppose

$$B_1 = \{b_5, b_2, b_1, b_7, b_3, b_9\}$$

and

$$B_2 = \{b_4, b_2, b_5, b_8\},$$

then

$$B_1 \cup B_2 = \{b_5, b_2, b_1, b_7, b_4, b_9, b_8, b_3\} = B.$$

Two things should be noted: the union of $B_1$ and $B_2$ is a new set (call it $B$), and every element in $B$ is either in $B_1$ or in $B_2$ (whereas some elements, such as $b_2$ and $b_5$, happen to be in both). As a special case of union, note that

$$\{a\} \cup \{b\} = \{a, b\}.$$

Here is one typical example of the way the notion comes up. Consider an event $E_1$ that may occur in various ways (such as getting a sum equal to 7 when a pair of dice is thrown) and another event $E_2$ that may also occur in one or more different ways (such as the ways in which 11 can come up when tossing a pair of dice). Then $E_1 \cup E_2$ represents the occurrence of either event (such as the event of getting either 7 or 11 when a pair of dice is tossed). As a rather different example, suppose $L$ is the set of all integers less than 8 and $G$ is the set of all integers greater than 5. Then $L \cup B$ is the set of all numbers that are either less than 8 or greater than 5. (Notice that some integers, such as 6 and 7, happen to be both.)

This notion is readily generalized to more than two sets. For example, consider the collection* of sets

$$\mathfrak{U} = \{\{1\}, \{1, 2, 3\}, \{1, 2\}, \{2, 3\}, \{4\}\}.$$

Then we write

$$\bigcup_{X \in \mathfrak{U}} X = \{1\} \cup \{1, 2, 3\} \cup \{1, 2\} \cup \{2, 3\} \cup \{4\} = \{1, 2, 3, 4\},$$

which may be read, "the union of the sets $X$ where $X \in \mathfrak{U}$." The sets of the collection $\mathfrak{U}$ are called the *components* of the union.

An alternate notation, sometimes used for this set, is

$$\cup \{X \mid X \in \mathfrak{U}\} = \{1, 2, 3, 4\}.$$

As another example, let $S$ be any nonempty (to make it interesting) set.

---

* We mean no more than a set of sets (that is, a set whose "elements" happen to be sets themselves); however, the expression "collection of sets" is often used because it sounds better. A set whose elements are themselves sets if often written in italics, boldface, or in German script, as shown, as a reminder that we are dealing with a set of sets; however, advanced texts often do not consider the distinction worth making and, indeed, often do not even make typographic distinctions between elements and sets, writing $x \in y$ rather than $x \in Y$.

Then as brought out previously, $P^S$ represents the set of all subsets of $S$. The reader may readily convince himself that

$$S = \bigcup_{X \in P^S} X;$$

that is to say, every set $S$ is the union of all its subsets. Furthermore, notice that every union of sets contains each of its components; thus, for example,

$$A \subseteq A \cup B \quad \text{and} \quad B \subseteq A \cup B.$$

It is interesting to note that $\mathfrak{U}$ may be regarded as a collection of names of sets. For example, when we wish to talk of the second set in this collection, we usually say, "Consider the set $\{1, 2, 3\} \ldots$," where what appears after the word "set" is a name, just as the word "set" itself is a name of something.

Now, we may just as well rename the sets in $\mathfrak{U}$, calling them $A_\alpha$, $A_\beta$, $A_\gamma, \ldots$. For this purpose we introduce a set of names $\mathfrak{N}$; the elements of $\mathfrak{N}$ will be denoted $\alpha, \beta, \gamma, \ldots$ and will be called names of sets. Evidently, the process of assigning names from the set $\mathfrak{N}$ is tantamount to assigning a subscript or index to each set considered. Thus, the set $\mathfrak{N}$ will be called an *index set* and the process of assigning names from $\mathfrak{N}$ will be called *indexing*, the individual names being called *indices*. The collection of sets to which names have been assigned is said to have been *indexed by* $\mathfrak{N}$. This collection is usually symbolized $\{A_\alpha\}_{\alpha \in \mathfrak{N}}$. The union of such a collection of sets is symbolized $\bigcup_{\alpha \in \mathfrak{N}} A_\alpha$. By definition, then, $x \in \bigcup_{\alpha \in \mathfrak{N}} A_\alpha$ if and only if $x$ is an element of $A_\alpha$ for at least one $\alpha$.

A common and useful set of names or indices often used in mathematics is the set

$$\mathfrak{N} = \{1, 2, 3, \ldots\}.$$

This set (considered, now, merely as a set of *labels*) has the obvious advantage that we won't run short of labels in any finite (real-world) applications, and not even in some infinite (though denumerable)* ones. With this understanding, we may write

$$\bigcup_{\alpha \in \mathfrak{N}} A_\alpha = A_1 \cup A_2 \cup A_3 \cup \cdots$$

or, sometimes,

$$\bigcup_{i=1}^{\infty} A_i = A_1 \cup A_2 \cup A_3 \cup \cdots.$$

In the event that $\mathfrak{N}$ is finite, the following notation is sometimes used:

$$\bigcup_{i=1}^{n} A_i = A_1 \cup A_2 \cup \cdots \cup A_n.$$

---

* Interestingly enough, the set of all points on a line just between 0 and 1 cannot be indexed by $\mathfrak{N}$; $\mathfrak{N}$ doesn't contain enough names to label all these points. The number of points is said to be *nondenumerable* (uncountable). We cannot go into a full discussion of infinite sets here; however, there is a fine discussion of this in Chapter 12 of Reference 4. See also the proof in Chapter 4 of Reference 13.

Though these are rather convenient notations, they are apt to lead to confusion unless we remember that the symbols 1, 2, 3, . . . are merely names or labels and that we could just as well use $\alpha, \beta, \gamma, \ldots$. In other words, it is important not to cloud the issue with the introduction of arithmetical concepts but, rather, to confine ourselves strictly to set-theoretic concepts and notations. All concepts of arithmetic, beginning with the integers themselves, are ultimately definable in terms of purely set-theoretic concepts. To be correct, then, if we wish to use the integers with their usual connotation, we must first define them ("create" them), and we have not done so here.

## 3.2   Set Intersection

An operation between sets that is, in some respects, analogous to the operation of multiplication between numbers is the operation of *intersection*, symbolized "$\cap$". The intersection of two sets, $A \cap B$,* is a set all of whose elements are simultaneously in *both A and B*. Symbolically,

$$A \cap B = \{x \mid x \in A \text{ and } x \in B\}.$$

Graphically, the intersection of two sets may be pictured as shown in Figure 3 by the shaded area.

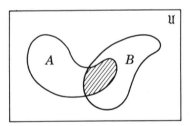

**Figure 3.** The set $A \cap B$ (shaded).

In the case of the sets $B_1$ and $B_2$ described in Section 3.1, we obtain

$$B_1 \cap B_2 = \{b_2, b_5\} = C.$$

It is seen that $C$ contains those, and only those, elements that are common to $B_1$ and $B_2$. And for the sets $L$ and $G$ we have

$$L \cap G = \{6, 7\}.$$

---

* Some authors refer to this as the set-theoretic or logical (Boolean) product of $A$ and $B$. This is rather misleading, for the resemblance between $\cap$ and $\cdot$ is no greater than the resemblance between $\cup$ and $+$. However, it seems to have become established terminology in many circles.

Obviously, if the two sets $A$ and $B$ do not "overlap" (have no elements in common)—we say they are *disjoint*—then

$$A \cap B = \mathfrak{E}.$$

That is to say, $A \cap B$ contains no elements (see Figure 2(a)). If these sest represent events, then we say the events are "mutually exclusive." (This will be discussed again in Chapter 6.)

The notion of intersection may be generalized in a manner similar to the case discussed above for union. We merely state the generalized definition here.

We will say that $x \in \cap_{\alpha \in \mathfrak{N}} A_{\alpha}$ if, and only if, $x \in A_{\alpha}$ for every $\alpha$. The sets of the collection of sets, $\mathfrak{N}$, are often called the *factors* of the intersection. It is easy to see that an intersection of sets is contained in each of its factors. Thus, for example,

$$A \cap B \subseteq A \quad \text{and} \quad A \cap B \subseteq B.$$

## 3.3   Symmetric Difference of Two Sets

There is also an operation between sets that is somewhat analogous to the arithmetical operation of subtraction. The set shown shaded in Figure 4(a) is the intersection of the complement of $A$ (that is, those elements *not*

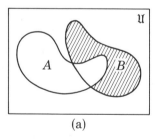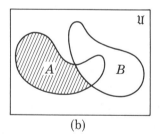

|     |     |
| --- | --- |
| (a) | (b) |

*Figure 4.* The "difference" of two sets. (a) The set $B - A$ (shaded). (b) The set $A - B$ (shaded).

in $A$) with $B$, namely, $\bar{A} \cap B$. This is the set of those elements in $B$ that are not in $A$; it is as though the elements of $A$ that are also in $B$ had been "subtracted out," and this set is often written as $B - A$. If $A \subseteq B$, then $B - A$ is called the *relative complement* of $A$ or, in this case, the complement of $A$ relative to $B$. As mentioned before, $\mathfrak{U} - A$ is called simply the complement of $A$, namely, $\bar{A}$. We emphasize again that, strictly speaking, every complement is relative to some other set. When the set is understood to be $\mathfrak{U}$, however, it is customary to write $\mathfrak{U} - A$ simply as $\bar{A}$. The set $A - B$ is shown in Figure 4(b). It is important to bear in mind, of course, that the "minus" sign appearing here is not the same as the minus sign of arithmetic.*

Incidentally, notice that by regarding the relation

$$A + \bar{A} = \mathfrak{U}$$

as an equation in the algebraic sense, we may use the methods of ordinary algebra to write

$$\bar{A} = \mathfrak{U} - A,$$

which happens to be true. However, there is a danger in this, since, for any nonempty set $A$,

$$A + A = A \qquad (not\ 2A,\ \text{as in algebra})$$

when "$+$" is interpreted as "$\cup$", which leads to the contradiction

$$A = A - A = \mathfrak{E};$$

also,

$$A \cdot A = A \qquad (not\ A^2,\ \text{as in algebra})$$

when "$\cdot$" is interpreted as "$\cap$".

Of course, no harm is done if we remember that the "addition," "multiplication," and "minus" signs, here borrowed from ordinary algebra, are being used in a very special sense. Indeed, this very notation *is* used in a type of algebra called Boolean algebra (after the mathematician George Boole), which bears a close relation (see Section 3.7) to set theory.

As pointed out above, when we speak of the set of elements in $A$ or $B$, it is always the inclusive "or" that is meant. We are now in a position to symbolize the use of the exclusive "or." This may be done in terms of the union of the two sets shown *shaded* in Figures 4(a) and 4(b),

$$(A - B) \cup (B - A).$$

This set, shown shaded in Figure 5, is called the symmetric difference of $A$ and $B$. It is the set of all those elements in $A$ or $B$, but *not* in both. There is no standard symbol for the symmetric difference of two sets, as there is for union and intersection. We find the notation

$$A \triangle B = (A - B) \cup (B - A)$$

---

* Bearing this in mind, we should not be surprised to discover that one may "subtract out" an "infinite "number of elements from an "infinite" set without decreasing the "number" of elements in the set. For example, given the set

$$N = \{1, 2, 3, 4, \ldots\}$$

one may "subtract out" or "delete" every even number in the set (there are, of course, an infinite number of these elements) and be left with a set containing just as many elements as before. Thus, $N - E$ may be placed into one-to-one correspondence with $N$. (See the second footnote in this chapter.)

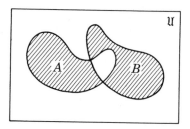

**Figure 5.** The set $(A - B) \cup (B - A)$—shaded.

convenient, but the reader is at liberty to supply his own notation. Incidentally, a comparison of Figure 5 with Figures 2(b) and 3 shows that $A \triangle B = (A \cup B) - (A \cap B)$. This does *not*, of course, constitute a *proof* of the relation. A *proof* would have to be based on set-theoretic notions, not on diagrams.

## 3.4 Additional Examples of Sets

Some further examples of sets are listed below for illustrative purposes. The interested reader may wish to generate several additional sets by applying set-theoretic operations to those given below:

1. the set of all integers between 1 and 100, inclusive;

2. the set of all even primes;

3. the set of all even numbers whose squares are odd;

4. the set of all real numbers between 0 and 1;

5. the set of all points between 0 and 1 on the Euclidean line; and,

6. the set of all possible outcomes when a coin is tossed twice in a row.

We shall use subscripts on $S$ to correspond with the numbering of the examples above. Thus, the first example may be symbolized

$$S_1 = \{1, 2, 3, 4, 5, \ldots, 100\}$$

—that is, extensively. Alternatively,

$$S_1 = \{x \mid x \text{ is an integer and } 1 \leqslant x \leqslant 100\},$$

where "$1 \leqslant x \leqslant 100$" is to be rendered, "$x$ is greater than or equal to 1 and less than or equal to 100: that is, $x$ is between 1 and 100 inclusive."

The second example, mentioned before, illustrates a set containing just one element, for there is exactly one even prime number, namely, 2, so that

$$S_2 = \{2\}.$$

The set of the third example is empty:

$$S_3 = \mathfrak{E},$$

since the square of an even number is even. This may be seen as follows. Any (every) even number can be written as $2n$ (where $n = 0, 1, 2, \ldots$). Squaring this, we obtain $4n^2$, which is clearly divisible by 2 and, hence, is also even. Thus, there are no even numbers whose squares are odd. The reader may readily verify, furthermore, that the square of any odd number must be odd. (Hint: Every odd number is of the form $2n - 1$, where $n = 1, 2, \ldots$.)

The so-called *real numbers* of example 4 are comprised of the *rational* (from the root word "ratio") numbers and the irrational (not expressible as a ratio) *numbers*. Some examples of rational numbers are 1/3, 9/7, 95/263, 8/1, and 6/3—as well as the negatives of these numbers, of course.

Rational numbers of the type 8/1 and 6/3 are representative of a class of rational numbers that can be shown to be isomorphic to (that is, have the same form as) the class of all positive integers; such numbers ordinarily are written simply as integers. We write 8/1 as 8 and 6/3 as 2 (the difference between 6/3 and 2 is no more significant than the difference between 4 and IV) The set of integers is made up of the positive whole numbers $1, 2, 3, \ldots$ (sometimes called natural numbers); the negative whole numbers $-1, -2, -3, \ldots$; and 0.

Some examples of irrational numbers are $\sqrt{2}$, $\sqrt[3]{2/5}$, $\sqrt{3}$, $1/\sqrt{2}$, $\pi$, $\sqrt{\pi}$, $1/\pi$, and $e$. The latter four numbers are further characterized as *transcendental numbers*. (There are more of these than there are rational numbers.*) These latter numbers have the property that they can never be roots (solutions) of algebraic equations with rational coefficients. The irrational and transcendental numbers belong to the class of so-called real numbers (as distinguished from the so-called imaginary numbers like $\sqrt{-1}$, which are really no more "imaginary" than "real" numbers—but the names have stuck). The real numbers include as special cases such numbers as $\sqrt{4} = 2$, which happens to be rational, just as the rationals include such special cases as $6/3 = 2$, which happen to be integral. The situation may be outlined as follows:

Complex numbers

I. Imaginary numbers

II. Real numbers

    1. Irrational numbers

        A. Transcendental numbers

        B. Surds

---

* By "more" is meant, roughly, that it is impossible to form a one-to-one correspondence between the set of all integers and the set of all transcendental numbers such that the latter set will be exhausted. (See the second footnote in this chapter.)

2. Rational numbers
    A. Fractions
    B. Integers
        (a) Negative integers
        (b) Positive integers
            (1) Natural numbers
            (2) Sets

Frequently, it is impossible to define a set by enumeration. The fourth example is such a case, because $S_4$ contains infinitely many elements. Indeed, it can be shown that $S_4$ contains "more" elements than the set of all positive integers, which also contains infinitely many elements.* Nevertheless, the set is readily defined as

$$S_4 = \{x \mid 0 < x < 1\},$$

which says that $x \in S_4$ if, and only if, $0 < x < 1$. In words, "$x$ is an element of the set $S_4$ (or, belongs to $S_4$), if, and only if, $x$ is a (real) number between zero and one."

The final example, by contrast, is a set most easily defined by enumeration (rather than description). Tossing a coin twice in a row we might get heads both times (HH), a head on the first toss and tails on the second (HT), vice versa (TH), or finally, tails both times (TT). Thus

$$S_6 = \{\text{HH, HT, TH, TT}\}$$

is the set defining *all* the *possible* outcomes of two tosses of a coin (neglecting, of course, such "freak" outcomes as the coin's landing on its edge).

## 3.5 Summary of Terminology

The major concepts of elementary set theory are summarized below for easy reference.

    (a) A set may be defined: in *extension* (by *enumeration*)—for example, $S = \{2, 4, 6, 8\}$; or in *intension* (by *description*)—that is, stating a property "collectively" shared by the elements, as for example, $S = \{x \mid x \text{ is an even integer and } 0 < x < 10\}$.

    (b) If $S = \{x \mid x \in A\}$, where it is understood that $A \subseteq \mathfrak{U}$, then $\bar{S}$, the *complement* of $S$, equals $\{x \mid x \notin A\}$. That is, the complement of a set $S$ is the set consisting of all of those elements that are *not* members of $S$.

    (c) The set of all elements in the "universe of discourse" is called the *universal set* $\mathfrak{U}$.

* See the previous footnote.

(d) The *empty* or *null* set, $\mathfrak{E}$, is the set that does not contain any elements —for example, $A \cap \bar{A} = \mathfrak{E}$.

(e) If every $x \in A$ is also an $x \in B$, then $A$ is a *subset* of (*is included in*) $B$, symbolized $A \subseteq B$. Every set, including the universal and null sets, is a subset of itself and, in particular, the null set is a subset of every set. Furthermore, every set of $n$ elements has $2^n$ subsets.

(f) Two sets are *equal*, $A = B$, if, and only if, every $x \in A$ is also an $x \in B$ and, conversely, every $x \in B$ is an $x \in A$. Alternatively, if both $A \subseteq B$ and $B \subseteq A$ hold, then $A = B$ (and vice versa).

(g) The union of two sets $A \cup B = \{x \mid x \in A \text{ or } x \in B\}$, where the "or" is interpreted as the inclusive "or." This is readily extended to the the case of more than two sets as follows.

$$\bigcup_{\alpha \in I} A_\alpha = \{x \mid x \in A_a \text{ or } x \in A_b \text{ or } \cdots\},$$

where $I$ is an *index set*, or set of "labels" to be attached to sets. Where $I = \{1, 2, 3, \ldots\}$, we sometimes see

$$\bigcup_{i=1}^{\infty} A_i = A_1 \cup A_2 \cup A_3 \cup \cdots.$$

In particular, when $I = \{1, 2, 3, \ldots, n\}$,

$$\bigcup_{i=1}^{n} A_n = A_1 \cup A_2 \cup \cdots \cup A_n.$$

(h) The *intersection* of two sets $A \cap B = \{x \mid x \in A \text{ and } x \in B\}$. This is readily extended to the case of more than two sets; symbolically,

$$\bigcap_{\alpha \in I} A_\alpha = \{x \mid x \in A_a \text{ and } x \in A_b \text{ and } \cdots\},$$

where $I$ is an index set; in this case $I = \{a, b, c, \ldots\}$. Conventions similar to those under (g) apply where $I = \{1, 2, \ldots\}$ or $I = \{1, 2, \ldots, n\}$.

(i) Two sets are said to be *disjoint* if there is no $x \in A$ that is also an $x \in B$. Alternatively, if $A \cap B = \mathfrak{E}$ the sets are said to be disjoint.

(j) The *difference* of two sets, $A - B$, is the set consisting of all of those elements in $A$ that are not also in $B$. Thus, $A - B = A \cap \bar{B}$. When $B \subseteq A$, this is also called the complement of $B$ relative to $A$. The complement of $A$ relative to $\mathfrak{U}$, $\mathfrak{U} - A$ (where, of course, $A \subseteq \mathfrak{U}$), is simply called the complement of $A$, symbolized $\bar{A}$.

(k) The *symmetric difference* of two sets, $(A - B) \cup (B - A)$, is the set consisting of those elements that are in $A$ or in $B$, but not in both. Thus, $(A - B) \cup (B - A) = (A \cap \bar{B}) \cup (\bar{A} \cap B)$.

## 3.6 Some Theorems

This section summarizes the more important results established previously and presents some basic theorems regarding sets. The industrious reader may wish to establish these and may thus consider them as part of the exercises at the end of this chapter. A few sample proofs are given. Alternatively, the results 1 through 23 may be taken for granted and used to do the exercises.

Several of the results below become obvious on our merely drawing the appropriate "picture"; however, this does *not* constitute a *proof*. An adequate proof (one will be sketched below) should make use *only* of the definitions and relations previously established. The picture may be a visual aid, but it *can* be deceiving. Many readers, no doubt, are familiar with the fallacious proof, often given in puzzle books, that every triangle is isosceles. The fallacy results from placing too great a reliance on reasoning from a sketch.

1. For any set $A$, $\mathfrak{E} \subseteq A$ and $A \subseteq \mathfrak{U}$. That is, the empty set is a subset of every set and every set is a subset of the universal set.

2. For any set $A$, $A \subseteq A$; that is, every set is a subset of itself.

3. For any set $A$, $A \cap A = A$ and $A \cup A = A$.

4. For any two sets, $A$ and $B$, $A \cup B = B \cup A$ and $A \cap B = B \cap A$ (commutative law).

5. For any three sets $A$, $B$, and $C$, $A \cup (B \cup C) = (A \cup B) \cup C$ and $A \cap (B \cap C) = (A \cap B) \cap C$ (associative law); hence in general the parentheses may simply be omitted and we write $A \cup B \cup C$ and $A \cap B \cap C$.

6. For any three sets $A$, $B$, and $C$, $A \cup (B \cap C) = (A \cup B) \cap (A \cup C)$ and $A \cap (B \cup C) = (A \cap B) \cup (A \cap C)$ (distributive law; notice that there are two forms).

7. $\mathfrak{E} \cup A = A$; $\mathfrak{E} \cap A = \mathfrak{E}$. (Is this also true when, in particular, $A = \mathfrak{E}$ or $A = \mathfrak{U}$?)

8. $\mathfrak{U} \cup A = \mathfrak{U}$; $\mathfrak{U} \cap A = A$. (True for $A = \mathfrak{U}$? for $A = \mathfrak{E}$?)

9. $A \cup \bar{A} = \mathfrak{U}$; $A \cap \bar{A} = \mathfrak{E}$. (True for $A = \mathfrak{E}$? for $A = \mathfrak{U}$?)

10. $\bar{\bar{A}} = A$. (This says that the complement of the complement of any set $A$ is $A$ itself.)

11. $\bar{\mathfrak{U}} = \mathfrak{E}$.

12. $(A \cap B) \subseteq A$;* $(A \cap B) \subseteq B$.

---

* We have here another reason for agreeing to regard the empty set as contained in every set: it allows us to reconcile this statement with the statement that $A \cap B$ may be empty even though neither $A$ nor $B$ is empty; for example, see the second relation under item 9 above. Recall that *in algebra* whenever you have $a \cdot b = 0$ you *must* have either $a = 0$ or $b = 0$, possibly both.

13. $A \subseteq (A \cup B)$; $B \subseteq (A \cup B)$.

14. $\overline{A \cup B} = \bar{A} \cap \bar{B}$; $\overline{A \cap B} = \bar{A} \cup \bar{B}$ (De Morgan's law: the complement of the union of two sets is equal to the intersection of their complements, and the complement of the intersection is equal to the union of the complements).

15. $A - B = A \cap (\mathfrak{U} - B)$.

16. $A - (B - C) = (A - B) \cup (A \cap C)$.

17. $(A - B) - C = A - (B \cup C)$.

18. $A \cap (B - C) = (A \cap B) - (A \cap C)$.

19. $A \cup (B - C) = (A \cup B) - (C - A)$.

20. $A = (A \cap B) \cup (A \cap \bar{B})$. (That is, any set $A$ can be partitioned into disjoint sets, $A \cap B$ and $A \cap \bar{B}$.)

21. $A \cup B = (A \cap B) \cup (A \cap \bar{B}) \cup (\bar{A} \cap B)$.

22. $A \cap B = \mathfrak{U} - [(\mathfrak{U} - A) \cup (\mathfrak{U} - B)]$.

23. $(A_1 \cup A_2) \triangle (B_1 \cup B_2) \subseteq (A_1 \triangle B_1) \cup (A_2 \triangle B_2)$.

It is to be noticed that the operators $\cap$ and $\cup$ bear a certain resemblance to the operators "$\cdot$" and "$+$" of ordinary algebra, as mentioned previously. But there are also certain marked contrasts. Thus, item 4 is similar to the familiar algebraic relations $x \cdot y = y \cdot x$ and $x + y = y + x$. The same goes for item 5. Notice, however, that algebra has only one distributive law, namely $x \cdot (y + z) = x \cdot y + x \cdot z$, and that there is no analogue, in algebra, for the first relation in item 6. Notice too that in algebra whenever we have $x \cdot y = 0$ we conclude that either $x$ or $y$ (possibly both) must be zero; but item 9 shows that, with sets, we may have $A \cap B = \mathfrak{E}$ even though neither $A = \mathfrak{E}$ nor $B = \mathfrak{E}$. There is a similar result for matrices (cf. Chapter 5).

A rather important relation is given above by De Morgan's law. One form of this relation—the second relation under item 14—becomes clear when the sets $\bar{A} \cup \bar{B}$ and $\overline{A \cap B}$ are sketched as shown in Figures 6(a) and 6(b). In Figure 6(a) the set $\bar{A}$ is shown by the shading that slants *down* to the *left* and the set $\bar{B}$ by the shading that slants down to the *right*. Thus, everything *shaded* (in one way or another) represents $\bar{A} \cup \bar{B}$. In Figure 6(b) the *unshaded* region is evidently $A \cap B$ and, hence, the shaded area represents $\overline{A \cap B}$. On comparing the *shaded* regions in Figures 6(a) and 6(b), notice that they are the same (cover identical areas) and, hence, they represent the same set. That is, $\bar{A} \cup \bar{B} = \overline{A \cap B}$. As mentioned above, although these quasi-geometrical illustrations lend plausibility to certain relations between sets, they do not constitute *proofs* of these relations. As an example of the procedure used for proving theorems in set theory, a proof of the first relation under item 14 is given below. The reader may wish to test his understanding

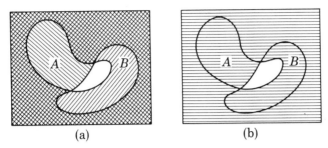

**Figure 6.** De Morgan's law. (a) The set $\bar{A} \cup \bar{B}$ (total shaded area). (b) The set $\overline{A \cap B}$ (shaded).

of the procedure by supplying his own proof of the second relation. Of course, any insights gained from Figures 6(a) and 6(b) may be used, but the (formal) proof itself should not involve any reference to such arbitrary sketches.

**Theorem.** For any two sets, $A$ and $B$,

$$\overline{A \cup B} = \bar{A} \cap \bar{B}.$$

PROOF. An equality between sets, such as $\overline{A \cup B}$ and $\bar{A} \cap \bar{B}$, may be established if it can be shown that the two sets include each other (that is, that *both* $\overline{A \cup B} \subseteq \bar{A} \cap \bar{B}$ *and* $\bar{A} \cap \bar{B} \subseteq \overline{A \cup B}$). To show that one set is included in (is a subset of) another, it is sufficient to show that *if* an element belongs to the first set, *then* it also belongs to the second set. (This follows from the definition of "inclusion.")

(a) Suppose $x \in \overline{A \cup B}$; then (why?)* $x \notin A$ and $x \notin B$ (that is, $x$ is neither in $A$ nor in $B$); thus, $x \in \bar{A}$ and $x \in \bar{B}$. Therefore $x \in \bar{A} \cap \bar{B}$, and so

$$\overline{A \cup B} \subseteq \bar{A} \cap \bar{B}.$$

(b) If, on the other hand, $x \in \bar{A} \cap \bar{B}$, then $x \in \bar{A}$ and $x \in \bar{B}$. Therefore $x \notin A$ and $x \notin B$; that is, $x \in \overline{A \cup B}$, and thus

$$\bar{A} \cap \bar{B} \subseteq \overline{A \cup B};$$

therefore,

$$\overline{A \cup B} = \bar{A} \cap \bar{B} \qquad \text{Q.E.D.}†$$

We give a few more examples.

---

* The reader should form the habit of asking this question after every "then" statement. Every statement made in a proof must be justified by appealing either to a definition, an axiom, or some previously established theorem.

† *Quod Erat Demonstrandum:* which was to be demonstrated.

**Theorem.** $A \cup (B \cap C) = (A \cup B) \cap (A \cup C)$.

PROOF. If $x \in A \cup (B \cap C)$, then either (i) $x \in A$, or (ii) $x \in B \cap C$, or (iii) both.

(i) If $x \in A$, then obviously $x \in A \cup B$ as well, and also $x \in A \cup C$. Hence, $x \in (A \cup B) \cap (A \cup C)$.

(ii) If $x \in B \cap C$, then $x \in B$ and $x \in C$. From the first fact (namely, that $x \in B$), $x \in A \cup B$, and from the second (that $x \in C$), $x \in A \cup C$. Hence, $x \in (A \cup B) \cap (A \cup C)$. Having shown that *if* $x \in A \cup (B \cap C)$, then $x \in (A \cup B) \cap (A \cup C)$, we have established that

$$A \cup (B \cap C) \subseteq (A \cup B) \cap (A \cup C).$$

The reader may finish the proof by showing that, also,

$$(A \cup B) \cap (A \cup C) \subseteq A \cup (B \cap C),$$

whence

$$A \cup (B \cap C) = (A \cup B) \cap (A \cup C).$$

Often a theorem can be proven much more simply. For example:

**Theorem.** $(A \cup B) - B = A \cap \bar{B}$.

PROOF

$(A \cup B) - B = (A \cup B) \cap \bar{B}$     (by item (j), in Section 3.5),

$(A \cup B) \cap \bar{B} = (A \cap \bar{B}) \cup (B \cap \bar{B})$      (by items 4 and 6 above),

$B \cap \bar{B} = \mathbb{C}$     (by item 9, above).

Therefore,

$(A \cup B) \cap \bar{B} = (A \cap \bar{B}) \cup \mathbb{C}$

$= A \cap \bar{B}$ (by items 4 and 7, above).

We give another example for which the reader should supply the justification at each step from among the items in Section 3.5 and the theorems listed above (items 1–23).

**Theorem.** $[A - (A \cap B)] \cap \overline{C} = A \cap (\overline{B \cup C})$.

PROOF

$$[A - (A \cap B)] \cap \overline{C} = [A \cap (\overline{A \cap B})] \cap \overline{C}$$

$$= [A \cap (\bar{A} \cup \bar{B})] \cap \overline{C}$$

$$= [(A \cap \bar{A}) \cup (A \cap \bar{B})] \cap \overline{C}$$

$$= (A \cap \bar{B}) \cap \overline{C}$$

$$= A \cap (\bar{B} \cap \overline{C})$$

$$= A \cap (\overline{B \cup C}).$$

## 3.7   Boolean Algebra

A familiar form of Boolean algebra involves two operators that may be symbolized by "·" and "+" and for which special laws are defined. A Boolean algebra will result if we identify $\mathfrak{E}$ with 0, and $\mathfrak{U}$ with 1, and define $A \cdot B$ to mean $A \cap B$ and $A + B$ to mean $A \cup B$. Then the following propositions are readily obtained.*

P-1: $A \cdot B = B \cdot A$; $A \cdot (B \cdot C) = (A \cdot B) \cdot C$.

P-2: $A + B = B + A$; $A + (B + C) = (A + B) + C$.

P-3: $A \cdot (B + C) = A \cdot B + A \cdot C$ and $A + (B \cdot C) = (A + B) \cdot (A + C)$.

P-4: $A + 0 = A$.

P-5: $A \cdot 0 = 0$.

P-6: $A + 1 = 1$.

P-7: $A \cdot 1 = A$.

P-8: $A + A = A$.

P-9: $A \cdot A = A$.

P-10: $A + \bar{A} = 1$.

P-11: $A \cdot \bar{A} = 0$.

Some subset (for example, P-1, P-2, P-3, P-4, P-7, P-10, and P-11) of this set of 11 propositions may be taken as a basic set of postulates to form the starting point of a familiar type of Boolean algebra. Indeed, it is possible to begin the axiomatic development of Boolean algebra with just a single operation, say $+$, defining any other operations in terms of this one, and using a still smaller list of basic postulates. While such relations as P-5, P-6, P-8, and P-9 may be proved from the remaining propositions, we state them here as additional propositions, for convenience. Notice that a good many more propositions may be stated by simply translating propositions 1 through 23 of Section 3.6 into the current "language."

Boolean algebra is sometimes called the *algebra of statements*. The reason for this may be seen from the following application.

We let $A, B, C, \ldots, X$ stand for statements that may be either true or false. Thus, $A$, or $X$ if you prefer, is a variable that may assume one and only one of two mutually exclusive values: $T$ (True) or $F$ (False). In Boolean algebra the values are taken to be 1 and 0 and we'll adopt the rule:

$$X = \begin{cases} 1 & \text{if and only if } X \text{ is a true statement,} \\ 0 & \text{if and only if } X \text{ is a false statement.} \end{cases}$$

* Alternately, some applications of Boolean-type algebras use the exclusive "or," where $+$ is equivalent to $(A - B) \cup (B - A)$. Notice that postulate P-8 then becomes $A + A = 0$.

Now, if $X$ and $Y$ are two different statements, there are exactly four possibilities: (1) both are true; (2) the first is true and the second false; (3) the first is false and the second true; (4) both are false. If $X \cdot Y$ is interpreted as the compound statement, $X$ *and* $Y$, when should this compound statement be regarded as true? Evidently, when (and only when) both $X$ and $Y$ are true. The four possibilities are shown in the first two columns of Table 3.1, and the values assumed by $X \cdot Y$ under the various possibilities are shown in the third column. Table 3.2 shows the situation for $+$, interpreted as the inclusive *or*. (0 means *false* and 1 means *true*, remember.)

| $X$ $Y$ | $X \cdot Y$ |
|---------|-------------|
| 1   1   | 1           |
| 1   0   | 0           |
| 0   1   | 0           |
| 0   0   | 0           |

| $X$ $Y$ | $X + Y$ |
|---------|---------|
| 1   1   | 1       |
| 1   0   | 1       |
| 0   1   | 1       |
| 0   0   | 0       |

***Table 3.1.*** The *and* function     ***Table 3.2.*** The *or* function

Finally, if a statement is true, its negation is evidently false. We interpret $\bar{X}$ as the negation of $X$, so that when $X = 0$, $\bar{X} = 1$ and when $X = 1$, $\bar{X} = 0$. This is depicted in Table 3.3.

| $X$ | $\bar{X}$ |
|-----|-----------|
| 0   | 1         |
| 1   | 0         |

***Table 3.3.*** Negation

In ordinary algebra, as you know, the $x$'s and $y$'s may take on any real numbers as values and so too for any function, $f(x, y)$, of $x$ and $y$. The situation here is considerably simpler since there are only two values a variable may take on: we can only have either $X = 1$ or $X = 0$. And if we have a function of two variables, such as $f(X, Y) = X + Y$, then $f(X, Y)$ likewise can take on only one of the two values 1 or 0. Furthermore, the multiplication and addition tables are simplicity itself, as shown by Tables 3.4 and 3.5.

| $\cdot$ | 1 | 0 |
|---------|---|---|
| 1       | 1 | 0 |
| 0       | 0 | 0 |

| $+$ | 1 | 0 |
|-----|---|---|
| 1   | 1 | 1 |
| 0   | 1 | 0 |

***Table 3.4.*** Boolean multiplication     ***Table 3.5.*** Boolean addition

Indeed, there is only one exception to the results of ordinary algebra and this is the rule that $1 + 1 = 1$. Since we have only two numbers, 0 and 1, at our disposal, $1 + 1$ must equal either 0 or 1. We don't *have* to take $1 + 1 = 1$, but we do so because if $X$ and $Y$ are both true ($X = 1$ and

$Y = 1$), then the compound statement $X$ *or* $Y$ is surely true ($= 1$), and we want to interpret $+$ to mean *or*. Nor is this the only situation in which we would want to use an "arithmetic" in which $1 + 1 = 1$. The fact that 1 is dominant in Table 3.5 recalls to mind an analogous situation in genetics. Thus, if the gene determining brown eyes, say, is dominant, the eye color of a child is determined by the entries in Table 3.6 when the eye-color gene contributed by each parent is as shown in the left and top margin.

|  | Brown | Blue |
|---|---|---|
| Brown | Brown | Brown |
| Blue | Brown | Blue |

*Table 3.6.* A genetic example

As an example of a situation calling for the rule $1 + 1 = 0$, let 1 stand for "odd" and 0 for "even." Then this rule says that odd (number) plus odd (number) equals even (number). The table for $\cdot$ remains the same—the only time the product of a pair of numbers is odd is if both factors are odd.

We will further agree that $\bar{1} = 0$ and $\bar{0} = 1$. This is in keeping with the fact that the negation of a truth is falsehood and conversely. Thus, if we have $X = 1$, signifying that $X$ is true, we may equally well write $\bar{X} = 0$, signifying that the negation of $X$ is false. Incidentally, perhaps the rule

$$A + (B \cdot C) = (A + B) \cdot (A + C)$$

makes somewhat more sense now when you interpret $+$ as *or* and $\cdot$ as *and*. In this same vein, consider the Boolean form of one of De Morgan's laws (see item 14, at the end of the previous section):

$$\overline{A \cdot B} = \bar{A} + \bar{B}.$$

If $A$ is the statement, "John will go to the beach," and $B$ is the statement, "The sun will be shining," then the above result reads:

> "It is not the case that John will go to the beach and the sun will be shining,"

which says the same thing as,

> "Either John will not go to the beach or the sun will not be shining."

Notice that the latter statement is true if: (1) John doesn't go to the beach and the sun is not shining; (2) John goes to the beach and the sun is not shining; (3) John doesn't go to the beach and the sun is shining. It is false only in the event that: John goes to the beach and the sun is shining. But this is also precisely the circumstance under which the statement:

> "It is not the case that John will go to the beach and the sun will be shining,"

is false.

The nice thing about interpreting Boolean algebra in this way, as an algebra of statements, is that it may be used to derive conclusions from given sets of statements in a purely "mechanical" (algebraic) way. For example, consider the following two statements.

(1) Either this reptile is not dangerous or the zoologist is mistaken or incompetent.

(2) The zoologist is not mistaken and he is not incompetent.

These may be translated into the following algebraic expressions ($D$ stands for the statement, "This reptile is dangerous"; $M$ for "The zoologist is mistaken"; and $I$ for "The zoologist is incompetent"):

(1) $\bar{D} + M + I = 1$,

(2) $\bar{M} \cdot \bar{I} = 1$.

Expression (2) may be written, equivalently, as

$$\overline{M + I} = 1$$

(using De Morgan's law), which is the same as

$$M + I = 0$$

(that is, if a negative statement is true its negation must be false). On substituting this result in expression (1) we find:

$$\bar{D} + 0 = 1$$

or

$$\bar{D} = 1,$$

which says that $\bar{D}$ is true—that is, the conclusion is, "This reptile is not dangerous." Additional examples are provided in the exercises.

Boolean algebra also offers a "mechanical" means of simplifying a complex set of statements. For example, suppose someone writes a will in which he bequeaths his estate to an heir under the following circumstances: the heir must be either married, or eighteen and a college student, or not married and eighteen, or married. If we let

$M$ = heir is to be married,

$E$ = heir is to be eighteen,

$C$ = heir is to be a college student,

then the conditions of the will may be symbolized:

$$\{M + (E \cdot C)\} + \{(\bar{M} \cdot E) + M\},$$

which, via Boolean algebra,

$$= \{(M + E) \cdot (M + C)\} + \{(\bar{M} + M) \cdot (E + M)\}$$

from the second form of P-3. Simplifying further, we have

$$= \{(M + E)(M + C)\} + \{1 \cdot (E + M)\}$$
$$= \{(M + E)(M + C)\} + \{(E + M) \cdot 1\}$$
$$= (M + E) \cdot \{(M + C) + 1\}$$
$$= (M + E) \cdot 1 = (M + E).$$

Thus, the benefactor could have made his wishes more clearly known by simply stating that he wanted the heir to receive the estate when the latter became 18 or married (or both).

We conclude this section with an example of the application of Boolean algebra to the design and analysis of networks and circuits such as occur in computers or the nervous system of organisms.

If two open switches that can be pulled shut by energizing a pair of electromagnets, $X$ and $Y$, are connected in series, as shown in the accompanying diagram, then the only time current will flow through the line $L$ will be when both $X$ and $Y$ are on. That is to say, the only time current will flow

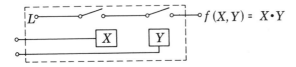

through $L$ is when current flows through both coils $X$ and $Y$ so that the switches are pulled shut. We will say $f(X, Y) = 1$ when the line $L$ is "hot," and call $f(X, Y)$ the output function. It is, of course, a function of the inputs and, as just stated, $f(X, Y) = 1$ if, and only if, $X = 1$ and $Y = 1$.

The next two figures illustrate the situation for the remaining two Boolean operations we have discussed. In the first case depicted, current will flow through $PQ$—that is, $g(X, Y)* = 1$—if either coil $X$ is "on" ($X = 1$) or coil $Y$ is on ($Y = 1$)—or also if they happen to be both energized.

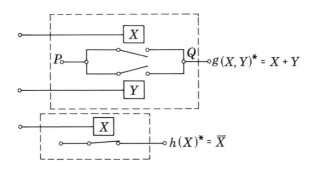

---

* We do not want to use $f(X, Y)$ again for this different function—no other significance is to be attached to the use of $g(X, Y)$ and of $h(X)$ in these figures.

In the second case, notice that the switch is closed. Thus, if $X$ is energized ($X = 1$), the circuit will be opened and $h(X)^* = 0$. Conversely, if $X$ is not energized ($X = 0$), then $h(X) = 1$—that is, the circuit is closed.

Some of the "laws" of Boolean algebra become almost trivial when $0$ and $1$ are interpreted in terms of open and closed switches. Some examples are shown below.

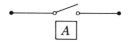

$A + 0 = 0 + A = A$

Notice that the open part of the circuit has no effect. That is, whether current flows from $P$ to $Q$ or not depends entirely on $A$ alone. Thus, this circuit accomplishes nothing more nor less than the simplified circuit:

to which it is completely equivalent. Some additional examples are (where $\equiv$ means the two circuits are equivalent):

$1 \cdot A = A$

$1 + A = 1$

$0 \cdot A = 0$

Boolean algebra may be used to advantage for simplifying circuits, as the following example shows. First, we simplify the diagrams a bit. The function $f(X, Y) = X \cdot Y$ will be represented by the simple circuit element:

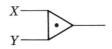

This element "fires" if, and only if, both $X$ and $Y$ are "fired." The function $g(X, Y) = X + Y$ will be represented by the element:

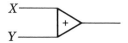

and, finally, $h(X) = \bar{X}$ is represented by:

Now, consider the circuit shown below, which has been designed to perform some logical function.

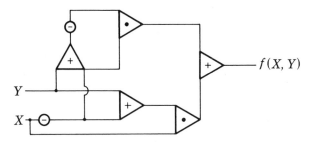

The question is: Can this circuit be reduced to a simpler one that will result in the same function? The first step in answering this question consists in writing out the Boolean function from an examination of the circuit. The way to do this is to examine the elements one at a time, to see what goes in and what comes out, starting near the inputs $X$ and $Y$. The results are shown below, on a single diagram.

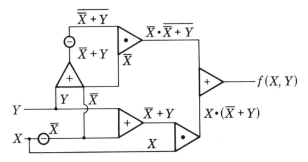

Thus, the output

$$f(X, Y) = X \cdot (\bar{X} + Y) + \bar{X} \cdot (\overline{\bar{X} + Y}).$$

We now use Boolean algebra to simplify the expression on the right.

$$f(X, Y) = X \cdot (\bar{X} + Y) + \bar{X} \cdot (X \cdot \bar{Y}).$$

This result follows from the Boolean expression of De Morgan's law ($\overline{X + Y}$ $= \bar{X} \cdot \bar{Y}$) and the fact that $\bar{\bar{X}} = X$. Next,

$$\begin{aligned}
f(X, Y) &= X \cdot (\bar{X} + Y) + (\bar{X} \cdot X) \cdot \bar{Y} \\
&= X \cdot (\bar{X} + Y) + 0 \cdot \bar{Y} \\
&= X \cdot (\bar{X} + Y) \\
&= X \cdot \bar{X} + X \cdot Y = 0 + X \cdot Y \\
&= X \cdot Y,
\end{aligned}$$

and the circuit has been simplified to:

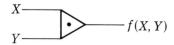

This circuit accomplishes exactly what the original circuit accomplishes, but much more simply, of course.

## EXERCISES

1.  (a) Prove $\mathfrak{U} \subseteq \mathfrak{U} \cup \mathfrak{E}$.
    (b) Prove $\mathfrak{E} \subseteq \mathfrak{U} \cup \mathfrak{E}$.

2.  Prove that $A \subseteq A \cup B$. (Hint: Work from the definitions.) Is $B \subseteq A \cup B$ also?

3.  (a) If $B \subseteq A$ then $A \cup B = ?$ (Hint: Use sketches.)
    (b) *Prove* your result under (a) above.

4.  Prove that if $A \cup B = A$ then $B \subseteq A$.

5.  (a) Prove $A \cup \mathfrak{E} = A$.
    (b) Prove $A \cup \mathfrak{U} = \mathfrak{U}$.
    (c) Prove $A \cup A = A$. (Notice how this differs from ordinary algebra where $A + A = 2A$.)

6.  Let $\mathfrak{A}$ be a "family" (that is, set) of *sets*; describe (define) the set $\bigcup_{X \in \mathfrak{A}} X$.

7.  (a) Does every union of sets contain each of its components?
    (b) From $S = \bigcup_{X \in P^S} X$ can you conclude that every set is the union of all of its elements?

8. Prove (note the contrast with Exercise 2 above):
   (a) $(A \cap B) \subseteq A$.
   (b) $(A \cap B) \subseteq B$.

9. Prove:
   (a) $A \cap A = A$.
   (b) $A \cap \mathfrak{E} = \mathfrak{E}$.
   (c) $A \cap \mathfrak{U} = A$.

10. Prove that $A \cap B \subseteq A \cup B$.

11. If $A$ and $B$ are sets:
    (a) What is the greatest set included in both $A$ and $B$?
    (b) What is the smallest nonempty set included in both $A$ and $B$?
    (c) Why is it necessary to qualify (b) with the word "nonempty"?

12. (a) Prove that if $A \subseteq B$, then $A \cap B = A$. (Contrast with Exercise 3 above.)
    (b) Prove that if $A \cap B = A$, then $A \subseteq B$. (Contrast with Exercise 4 above.)

13. Show that $(A - B) \subseteq A$.

14. Prove that if $A \subseteq B$, then $A - B = \mathfrak{E}$.

15. Show that $(A - B) \cap B = \mathfrak{E}$.

16. Given any set $A$, consider the technique of forming the set $A \cup \{A\}$, which may be called the *successor* of $A$. Thus, starting with $\mathfrak{E}$, you may form the successor of $\mathfrak{E}$, $\mathfrak{E} \cup \{\mathfrak{E}\} = \{\mathfrak{E}\}$. Call this set 1. Then $1 \cup \{1\} = \{\mathfrak{E}\} \cup \{1\} = \{\mathfrak{E}, 1\}$ is the successor of 1, call this set 2. What is the successor of 2? Of 3?

17. Show that:
    (a) $(A \cup A) - A = \mathfrak{E}$; but
    (b) $A \cup (A - A) = A$.

18. Show that $B - \bar{A} = B \cap A$.

19. Show that $(B - A) \subseteq \bar{A}$.

20. Prove that if $A \cap B = \mathfrak{E}$, then $A \subseteq \bar{B}$.

21. Prove that $A \triangle B = (A \cup B) - (A \cap B)$ from $A \triangle B = (A \cap \bar{B}) \cup (\bar{A} \cap B)$.

22. Translate the following statements into expressions in Boolean algebra; transform into an equivalent simple expression and translate back to English.
    (a) Neither Tom nor Jim will marry Jane.
    (b) You cannot both dance and not pay the piper.
    (c) It is not true that mathematics is dull or not any fun.
    (d) That gambler is clever, but either they are not clever or they are dishonest. (Hint: The word "but" is a conjunction just like "and.")
    (e) He is either sincere or a good liar but he cannot be both.

23.  Given the premises:

   (i) These results are either not significant or due to some random error or, possibly, a breakdown in the equipment has occurred.

   (ii) The results are not due to random error and they are not due to a breakdown in the equipment.

   Derive the conclusion using Boolean algebra.

24.  Given the premises:

   (i) Either the results of the experiment are significant or the apparatus wasn't working properly or our theory is incorrect.

   (ii) Either the apparatus was working properly, and our theory is not incorrect or our computations are not correct.

   (iii) Our computations (have been checked and) are correct.

   Using Boolean algebra derive the conclusion:  The results of the experiment are significant.

25.  Given the premises:

   (i) We dare not commit ourselves to both the policies $P_1$ and $P_2$ or the cause will be lost.

   (ii) Either the cause will not be lost or our leader is mistaken in his judgment.

   (iii) Our leader's assistant has bungled but our leader is not mistaken in his judgment.

   (iv) We will commit ourselves to $P_1$.

   Derive the conclusion using Boolean algebra.

26.  Simplify the following statement using Boolean algebra. "This insurance policy is valid only if it is not true that it is not the case that the insured is over 21 or married or in a nonhazardous occupation and not over 21 or alternatively that he is 21 and single or in a nonhazardous occupation." Let $T$ = insured is over 21; $M$ = he is married; and $N$ = he is in a nonhazardous occupation.

The following problems are a bit more difficult in that they presuppose a firm grasp on the results 1 through 23 at the end of Section 3.6; furthermore, the proofs in several problems depend upon the results in prior problems.

27.  Show that:
   (a) $A \cap (B \cap C) = (A \cap B) \cap (A \cap C)$.
   (b) $A \cup (B \cup C) = (A \cup B) \cup (A \cup C)$.
   These results are sometimes called the *self-distributive laws*. (Contrast with the distributive laws, given in item 6, Section 3.6.)

28.  (a) Does $A \cap B = A \cap C$ imply that $B = C$?
   (b) Does $A \cup B = A \cup C$ imply that $B = C$?
   (c) Does $A = B$ imply that $A \cap C = B \cap C$?

29.  Show that:
   (a) If $A \subseteq C$ and $B \subseteq C$, then $A \cup B \subseteq C$.
   (b) If $C \subseteq A$ and $B \subseteq C$, then $C \subseteq A \cap B$.

30.  Show that $A \subseteq B$ if, and only if, $A \cup B = B$. (Hint: Use the result established under Exercise 29(a) above.)

31. Show that if $A \cup X = \mathfrak{U}$ and $A \cap X = \mathfrak{E}$, then $X = \bar{A}$.

32. Show that complementation is unique—that is, that one may sensibly speak of *the* complement of $A \subseteq \mathfrak{U}$. (Hint: Start out by supposing that $A$ has two complements, $A_1$ and $A_2$, and derive the result that $A_1 = A_2$. Thus, one may sensibly speak of *the* complement of $A$ since any "other" is identical to it. Recall that $A \cap \bar{A} = \mathfrak{E}$ and $A \cup \bar{A} = \mathfrak{U}$; only now each result will split into two expressions, since we have assumed two complements.)

33. Express the following intersection of sets as a single set:

$$\{x \mid x \geqslant -2\} \cap \{x \mid x < 4\} = ?$$

Notice that we may sketch the two sets on a scale as shown in the accompanying figure. Study the figure carefully (notice that one point is solid, signifying that that point belongs to the set, while the other is open). The set that these two sets is equivalent to is shown right *on* the scale itself.

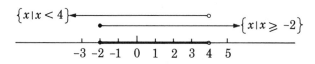

34. Express the following sets as a single set:

$$\{x \mid x > -4\} \cap \{x \mid x < 2\} = ?$$

35. Can you express the following union of sets as a single set?

$$\{x \mid x > 2\} \cup \{x \mid x < -4\}.$$

(Hint: This is the set of all $x$ except those in ———— ?)

36. Show that:
    (a) $A \bigtriangleup B = (A \cup B) \cap (\bar{A} \cup \bar{B})$.
    (b) $A \bigtriangleup B = (A \cup B) - (A \cap B)$.

37. It was mentioned in Section 3.7 that the postulates P-1, P-2, P-3, P-4, P-7, P-10, and P-11 form a basic set of postulates for a Boolean algebra and that the remaining propositions may be derived from these.
    (a) Prove P-8 using the appropriate postulates from among P-1, P-2, P-3, P-4, P-7, P-10, and P-11.
    (b) Prove P-9.
    (c) Prove P-6.

38. Show that 0 and 1 are complements of each other in Boolean algebra, just as $\mathfrak{E}$ and $\mathfrak{U}$ are complements of each other in set theory.

# 4/ Product Sets, Relations, Mapping, and Functions

## 4.1 Product Sets

So far we have discussed several methods of generating new sets from given sets (such as complementation, intersection, union). There is one more operation between sets to discuss.

If $A$ and $B$ are arbitrary sets, we define the *product set* $A \times B$ to be the collection of pairs $(a, b)$, in that order, such that $a \in A$ and $b \in B$, where $A$ and $B$ need not be different. Thus

$$A \times B = \{(a, b) \mid a \in A \text{ and } b \in B\}.$$

The pair $(a, b)$ is said to be an *ordered pair** (or *ordered couple*) and we take $(a, b) \neq (b, a)$ whenever $a \neq b$, by definition. Notice that the situation here is different from that in the case of the *set* $\{a, b\}$, since $\{a, b\} = \{b, a\}$—that is, in a set we do not distinguish the order of elements.

The following special case is instructive. Suppose $A$ and $B$ are distinct and each contains only a single element, say, $a$ and $b$, respectively. Then

$$A \times B = \{(a, b)\}.$$

Evidently, $A \times B \neq B \times A$; that is to say, the operation is not commutative. The reader may have come across such a situation before in the case of

---

* We choose to adopt the notion of an "ordered pair" *de novo* as is done here. However, it should be pointed out that an ordered pair $(a, b)$ is a special kind of set and can be defined solely in terms of the set-theoretic notions discussed previously. One way of doing this is to define $(a, b)$ as the set $\{\{a\}, \{a, b\}\}$. Once having defined such a pair, we may now define a triplet,

$$(a, b, c) = ((a, b), c),$$

and so on. Incidentally, notice that

$$(a, a) = \{\{a\}, \{a, a\}\} = \{\{a\}, \{a\}\} = \{\{a\}\}.$$

44

matrices; however, whereas matrix "multiplication" is associative, in general the set "product" is not—that is, $(A \times B) \times C \neq A \times (B \times C)$. Notice, however, that these sets are equivalent; for example,

$$(A \times B) \times C \sim A \times (B \times C) \qquad \text{and} \qquad A \times B \sim B \times A.$$

We will say that the ordered pair $(a, b)$ is identical to the ordered pair $(c, d)$ if, and only if, $a$ is identical to $c$ and $b$ is identical to $d$.

Thus.

$$(a, b) = (c, d) \qquad \text{if, and only if, } a = c \text{ and } b = d.$$

If $A$ consists of $m$ elements, $a_1, a_2, \ldots, a_m;$ and $B$ contains $n$ elements, $b_1, b_2, \ldots, b_n$, then $A \times B$ is a set consisting of the $mn$ elements $(a_i, b_j)$. More generally, if $A_1, A_2, A_3, \ldots, A_r$ are any sets, then

$$A_1 \times A_2 \times \cdots \times A_r = \prod_{i=1}^{r} A_i$$

(where $\prod$ may be read "product of") is defined to be the collection of $r$-tuples $(a_1, a_2, \ldots, a_r)$ such that the $i$th component, $a_i$, is an element of the $i$th set $A_i$.

Some examples will make matters clearer. Suppose $A = \{a_1, a_2, a_3\}$ and $B = \{b_1, b_2\}$. Then

$$A \times B = \{(a_1, b_1), (a_2, b_1), (a_3, b_1), (a_1, b_2), (a_2, b_2), (a_3, b_2)\}$$
$$= \{(a_1, b_1), (a_1, b_2), (a_2, b_1), (a_2, b_2), (a_3, b_1), (a_3, b_2)\}.$$

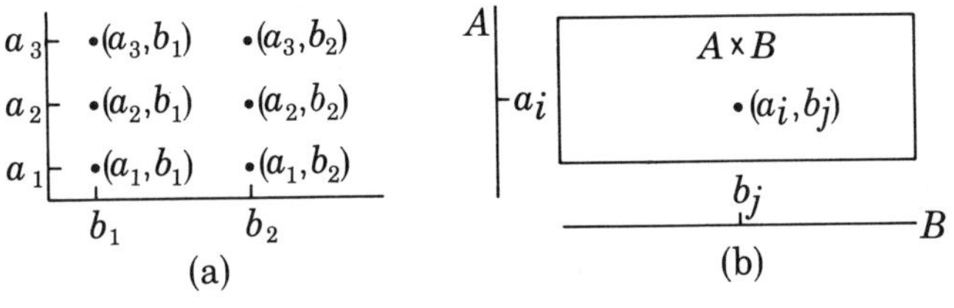

**Figure 7.** Product sets. (a) Example of a product set $A \times B$. (b) General case of $A \times B$.

The situation may be depicted as shown in Figure 7(a); the general case is shown in Figure 7(b). Notice that if $A$ contains $m$ elements and $B$ contains $n$, there are altogether $mn$ ordered couples in $A \times B$. Evidently, a set of ordered pairs may also be generated out of a single set. For example, given $A = \{a, b, c\}$, the following ordered pairs may be extracted:

$$(a, c) \qquad (b, c) \qquad (c, c)$$
$$(a, b) \qquad (b, b) \qquad (c, b)$$
$$(a, a) \qquad (b, a) \qquad (c, a)$$

The set of all ordered pairs whose elements are members of $A$ is usually referred to as the *Cartesian set* of $A$, denoted by $A \times A$. Thus, $(a, b) \in A \times A$ if, and only if, $a \in A$ and $b \in A$, where $a$ and $b$ need not be different. In the case of the present example,

$$A \times A = \{(a, c), (b, c), (c, c), (a, b), (b, b), (c, b), (a, a), (b, a), (c, a)\}.$$

Notice that a set of $m$ elements generates a Cartesian set of $m^2$ elements and that $A \times A$ has $2^{m^2}$ subsets (including $A \times A$ itself and $\mathfrak{E}$).

It should not be concluded that *any* collection of ordered pairs is a product set. Thus, for example,

$$\{(d, a), (e, a), (e, b), (e, c)\}$$

is *not* a product set, since any product set that contains $(d, a)$ and $(e, b)$ must also contain $(d, b)$.

## 4.2   Relations

Examples of relations abound: *father of, brother of, precedes, is shorter than, is less than, is greater than, is between*, and so on. The last mentioned is an example of a *ternary relation* (for example, we say $c$ is between $a$ and $b$—thus, three elements are involved); the former are all examples of *binary relations*. Characteristically, a binary relation involves the notion of two sets of things, together with a rule or criterion for deciding whether or not an object from one of the sets and an object from the other "belong together" in the relationship. We will confine our discussion here, and in the next section, to binary relations.

For example, consider the set of all men $M$, the set of all women $W$, and the relationship of marriage $R$. Evidently, this relationship can be used as a criterion for deciding whether a couple of people $(p_1, p_2)$, such that $p_1 \in M$ and $p_2 \in W$, belong together under the relationship $R$ or not (that is, are married or not). If $p_1$ is married to $p_2$, then we may write equally well $p_1 R p_2$ or $(p_1, p_2) \in R$—that is, the couple $(p_1, p_2)$ are in the relationship of marriage. In other words, since any binary relation will always determine the set of all couples such that each couple is in the relation, we can define the relation equally well by the set of couples that are in it (that is, extensionally rather than intensionally). Looked at in this way, $R$ is a *set*; it is, moreover, a *product set*. Evidently, the set of all possible couples of men and women, no matter what their relationship, will belong to the product set $M \times W$ so that, in particular, $R \subseteq M \times W$.

As another example, consider the relationship $H$, "husband of." This too is a subset of $M \times W$. It is a perfectly well-defined collection of elements (couples); indeed

$$H = \{(a, b) \mid b H a\}$$

—that is, $H$ is the set of all couples $(a, b)$ such that $b$ is the husband of $a$. Thus, for example, (Nefer-iti, Akh-en-aton) $\in H$ because the husband of Nefer-iti was Akh-en-aton, while (Cleopatra, Caesar) $\notin H$. Notice that, as opposed to such relations as "married to" and "spouse of," the present relation is asymmetric: that is, if $a\,H\,b$ then it is *not* the case that $b\,H\,a$. In other words, while $R$ consisted of ordered pairs, since $R \subseteq M \times W$, the order was not important;* here, it is.

A more familiar example of an asymmetric relation, perhaps, is given by the binary relation $G$, "greater than." This set $G$ is the set of all ordered pairs $(x, y)$ such that $y\,G\,x$—that is, $y$ is greater than $x$. Incidentally, notice the order here (another one of those little conventions). It is similar to the entry in an index (such as "subset, proper" or "subset, proper, definition" instead of "definition of proper subset"). Instead of "$y$ is greater than $x$" the convention is to use the equivalent expression "greater than $x$, $y$." If we are speaking about a single set, say the set $S$ of rational numbers, we then speak of the relation $G$ *on* $S$. If two sets, $A$ and $B$, are involved, we speak of a relation *from A to B*. In general, then, we see that a binary relation $H$, for example, couples certain members from the set of human males to certain members of the set of human females. Alternatively, it may be considered as a relation *on* a set of people. The relation $H$ may be identified with the set of all ordered pairs that belong to it since, for most purposes, knowledge of the set in extension is as good as knowledge of the relation $H$; and an ordered pair $(p_1, p_2)$ is a member of the enumerated set if, and only if, $p_2\,H\,p_1$. A relation, then, is a set and, moreover, a subset of a product set.

From the remark at the end of Section 4.1 we see that $2^{n^2}$ relations are, in general, possible among $n$ elements (including the relation that does not hold $R = \mathfrak{E}$, and the relation that holds between every pair of elements, $R = A \times A$).

To recapitulate, a binary relation $R$ is a set of ordered pairs such that $b\,R\,a$ if, and only if, $(a, b) \in R$, in which case $(a, b)$ is said to *satisfy* the relation $R$. More generally, given a set $A$ and a set $B$, *a binary relation from A to B* is a subset $R$ of ordered pairs in $A \times B$. Similarly, a relation from $A$ to $A$ is a subset of $A \times A$. In this case we speak of a relation *on* $A$. Evidently, if $R$ is a relation, and $S \subseteq R$, then $S$ is a relation. Furthermore, if $R$ and $S$ are relations, then $R \cap S$, $R \cup S$, and $R - S$ are relations; and so on. Thus, the theorems from set theory apply here, in the case of relations.

Let us consider some examples. Take $\mathfrak{U}$ as the set of natural numbers from one to five and consider the relation "is a multiple of" on $\mathfrak{U}$. This relation couples, say, 4 to 1, 4 to 2, and 4 to 4, since 4 is a multiple of 1 ($4 = 1 \times 4$), a multiple of 2 ($4 = 2 \times 2$), and a multiple of 4 ($4 = 4 \times 1$). Thus, we say, for example, that the ordered pair $(2, 4)$ satisfies or belongs to

---

* Thus, strictly speaking, we should write $R \subseteq (M \times W) \cup (W \times M)$.

the relation "is a multiple of." (Recall that if $R$ is the relation, then $R(2, 4)$ is to be read "is a multiple of two, four.") By the same token, there are only two multiples of 5 in $\mathfrak{U}$, namely, 1 (since $5 = 1 \times 5$) and 5 (since $5 = 5 \times 1$), and there are only two multiples of 3 and only one multiple of 1. Tabulating all the ordered couples belonging to the relation, we obtain

$$R = \{(1, 5),\ (5,5),\ (1, 4),\ (2, 4),\ (4, 4),\ (1, 3),\ (3, 3),\ (1, 2),\ (2, 2),\ (1, 1)\}.$$

Notice that $R$ is a subset of the Cartesian set of $\mathfrak{U}$:

$$\mathfrak{U} \times \mathfrak{U} = \{(1, 1),\ (1, 2),\ (1, 3),\ (1, 4),\ (1, 5),\ (2, 1),\ (2, 2),\ (2, 3),\ (2, 4),$$

$$(2, 5),\ (3, 1),\ \ldots,\ (4, 1),\ \ldots,\ (5, 1),\ (5, 2),\ (5, 3),\ (5, 4),\ (5, 5)\},$$

which contains 25 elements (ordered pairs).

The situation may be depicted in the form of a "graph" as shown in Figure 8; the Cartesian set of $\mathfrak{U}$ is shown by both closed and open circles and the elements belonging to $R$ are shown by solid circles alone.

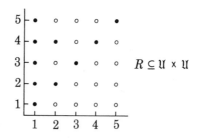

**Figure 8.** Graph of $R =$ "is a multiple of" (solid dots depict elements belonging to $R$).

Some additional notions will be found useful in discussing relations. As has been emphasized, a binary relation $R$ is a set of *ordered* couples $(a, b)$, which means that we distinguish between a "first" member and a "second" member in the couple. The set of all first members is called the *domain*, $\mathfrak{D}(R)$, of $R$ and the set of all second members is called the *counter domain*, $\mathfrak{C}(R)$, or *range* $\mathfrak{R}(R)$, of $R$. In the last example above, $\mathfrak{D} = \mathfrak{R} = \{1, 2, 3, 4, 5\}$. But this need not always be so. For example, if $B =$ "is a brother of"—that is, if $B$ is the relation that consists of all couples $(a, b)$ such that $b\ B\ a$—then $\mathfrak{R}(B)$ is the set of all *men* who have at least *one brother* or *one sister* while $\mathfrak{D}(B)$ is the set of all individuals (men or women) who have at least *one brother*. Finally, the *field*, $\mathfrak{F}(R)$, of a relation $R$ is the union of its domain with its counter domain.

As another example, consider the relation $R =$ "is greater by at least 2" on the set $\mathfrak{U} = \{1, 2, 3, 4, 5, 6, 7, 8, 9\}$. This set (relation) is shown in Figure 9. Here, clearly $\mathfrak{D}(R) \neq \mathfrak{R}(R) \neq \mathfrak{U}$.

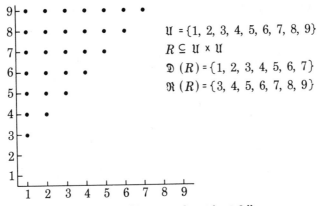

**Figure 9.** $R =$ "is greater by at least 2."

For the final notion, suppose we are given $a\ R\ b$; then the relation $R'$, such that $b\ R'\ a$, is called the *converse** of $R$. More formally: If $R$ is a relation on $A$ and if we define a relation $R'$ by the condition that $b\ R'\ a$ holds for $a, b \in A$ if, and only if, $a\ R\ b$ holds, then $R'$ will evidently be a relation on $A$; we call $R'$ the *converse* relation. Thus, given that $a\ H\ b$, where $H$ is the relation "husband of," we may equally well write $b\ W\ a$, where $W$ is the relation "wife of." The relation $H$ is said to be the converse of $W$, and vice versa. Similarly, the converse of "greater than" is "less than," and so on. Certain relations are their own converses—for example, "is a mate of"; these are the so-called symmetric relations. As an example, the converse of the relation $R$ shown in Figure 9 is shown in Figure 10.

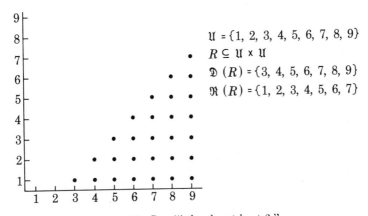

**Figure 10.** $R =$ "is less by at least 2."

---

* In the case of a function we use the term *inverse* (see Section 4.5).

## 4.3   Kinds of Relations

On a number of previous occasions we have used the terms "reflexive," "symmetric," and "transitive." These terms refer to certain properties of certain classes of relations. Besides the transitive, reflexive, and symmetric relations we will also discuss two important additional types of relations: the *equivalence* relations and *order* relations.

### 4.3.1   Reflexivity

If $R$ is a relation on $S$ and if for any $x \in S$ we have $x \, R \, x$, then $R$ is said to be a *reflexive relation* or, simply, *reflexive*. A typical example of a reflexive relation is the relation of inclusion, since for any set $A$ we always have

$$A \subseteq A.$$

Other examples of reflexive relations are the relations of congruence and similarity among triangles, since every triangle is obviously congruent to itself as well as similar to itself. Again, the relation "is a contemporary of" on a set of people is a reflexive relation.

If a relation is not reflexive, it is said to be *irreflexive*. Examples are common enough: "is the husband of," "is greater than," "is a proper subset of" are all irreflexive. We have already commented on the fact that the relation of membership, $\in$, is irreflexive. If a relation *may* be reflexive, but is not necessarily so, it is said to be *mesoreflexive* (or *nonreflexive*). An example is the relation "admires" on a set of people. Somewhat more formally: an irreflexive relation $R$ is a relation where $x \, R \, x$ for *no* $x \in S$, whereas a mesoreflexive relation $R$ is a relation where $x \, R \, x$ for *some*, but not all, $x \in S$.

### 4.3.2   Symmetry

If $R$ is a relation on $S$ and if, for any two elements in $S$ for which $x \, R \, y$ holds, $y \, R \, x$ also holds, then $R$ is said to be symmetric. Similarity and congruence, on a set of triangles, are both symmetric. Other examples are "is a spouse of," "is married to," "is a sibling of," "is as large as," and so on.

None of the relations "is a husband of," "is a wife of," "is larger than," "is a proper subset of," or "is an element of" is symmetric. A relation that is not symmetric is said to be *asymmetric*. More formally, if $R$ is a relation on $S$ and if for any two elements $x, y \in S$ for which we have $x \, R \, y$ we do not have $y \, R \, x$—that is, $x \, R \, y$ *implies* that $y$ is *not* in the relation $R$ to $x$—then we may say $R$ is *asymmetric*.

A relation such as "is a brother of" is not necessarily symmetric. For if $x$ is a brother of $y$, then $y$ is not necessarily the brother of $x$ ($y$ may be $x$'s sister). Notice, however, that this relation is not necessarily asymmetric either, for the fact that $x$ is a brother of $y$ does not *imply* that $y$ is not a brother of $x$. Thus, a relation such as this is said to be *mesosymmetric* (or *nonsymmetric*). Another example is "loves." Thus, a relation may fail to be symmetric either because it is asymmetric or because it is mesosymmetric.

Ordinary set inclusion is a mesosymmetric relation, for, obviously, the fact that $A \subseteq B$ does not *imply* that $B \nsubseteq A$; $B \subseteq A$ may, or may not, hold given that $A \subseteq B$ holds. In fact, we are dealing with a very interesting situation here. Should it happen that both $A \subseteq B$ and $B \subseteq A$, then, as we know, we conclude that $A = B$. Such a situation is described by saying that the relation of inclusion is *antisymmetric*. More formally, $R$ is *antisymmetric* on $S$ means that, for any two elements $x, y \in S$, if $x R y$ and $y R x$ then $x = y$—that is, $x$ and $y$ are identical. The relation "is less than or equal to," from elementary algebra, is an example of an antisymmetric relation on numbers. Incidentally, notice that a relation such as "is less than or equal in height to," on a set of people is *not* antisymmetric. Call this relation $H$; then even though it may happen that $x H y$ and $y H x$ (that is, persons $x$ and $y$ have the same height), it certainly does not follow from this that $x = y$ (that $x$ and $y$ are necessarily one and the same identical individual).

### 4.3.3 Transitivity

If $R$ is a relation on $S$ and if, for any three elements $x, y, z \in S$, $x R y$ and $y R z$ imply $x R z$, then $R$ is said to be a *transitive relation*. We have already commented on the fact that set inclusion (both proper and improper) is transitive. Other examples of transitive relations are: "is less than" on a set of numbers; "is later than" on a set of events; and so on.

A relation that is not transitive may be *intransitive* or *mesotransitive*. More formally, if $x R y$ and $y R z$ imply not-($x R z$), then $R$ is said to be *intransitive*. Examples are the relation "is married to" and the relation "is perpendicular to" on a set of lines in a plane (if $x$ is perpendicular to $y$ and $y$ is perpendicular to $z$, then $x$ is not perpendicular to $z$; it is, in fact, parallel to $z$).

Again, a relation $R$ on a set $S$ that is transitive for *some* elements in $S$ is said to be *mesotransitive* (or *nontransitive*). A couple of examples are "loves" and "is a relative of."

Needless to say, these properties are all independent of each other. That is to say, a relation may be reflexive without being transitive or symmetric, or it may symmetric without being reflexive or transitive, or it may be transitive without being reflexive or symmetric. The reader may readily convince himself of this by thinking of examples (relations) where one of these properties holds while the remaining two do not hold. For example, the relations "is less than" on the set of real numbers and "is the ancestor of" on a set of people are evidently transitive, but they are obviously neither symmetric nor reflexive. Furthermore, since transitivity results in three properties (transitive, intransitive, and mesotransitive), reflexivity results in three, and symmetry results in four, there are altogether thirty-six combinations, not all of which, of course, are possible—for example, if $R$ is asymmetric, then it cannot also be reflexive* (see the Exercises). Of these, we shall single out only a few for special study because of their importance. Before doing so, however, let us examine the graphs of some of these relations.

Let $R$ be a relation on a set $S$, then $R \subseteq S \times S$. Figure 11(a) portrays the case where $R$ is reflexive, and Figure 11(b) the case where $R$ is symmetric.

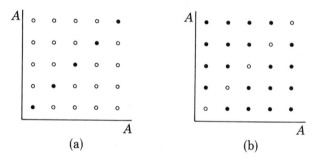

(a)                    (b)

**Figure 11.** The graph of a relation (solid dots depict elements belonging to $R$). (a) Reflexive relation, $R \subseteq A \times A$. (b) Symmetric relation, $R \subseteq A \times A$.

In Figure 11(a), notice that every solid point represents an ordered pair in which the first element is identical to the second. That is to say, for every element $x \in S$ we have an element $(x, x) \in R$; in other words: for every $x \in S$, we have $x \, R \, x$—which means nothing else than that $R$ is a reflexive relation on $S$. Notice that, as depicted, the relation also happens to be transitive and symmetric. The reader should not infer from this figure that, when $R$ is reflexive, $a \, R \, b$ *only* if $a = b$ (refer to Section 4.3.1). What *can* be said is that *if $R$ is a reflexive relation, then* the set of all points on the diagonal of the graph of $R \subseteq A \times B$ must belong to $R$. It is interesting to note that any subset of this "diagonal line" is an example of a relation that is *both* symmetric *and* antisymmetric. In Figure 11(b), the pattern of *solid* circles above the diagonal line of open circles appears as the "mirror image" of the pattern of *solid* circles below the diagonal line of open circles. Evidently, whenever we have $(a, b) \in R$, we also have $(b, a) \in R$. Actually, the figure contains more solid points than we really need. If $R$ is symmetric, all that is required is that for any solid point $(a, b) \in S$ there is a "reflected" solid

---

* Thus, while symmetry implies nothing about reflexivity, asymmetry implies irreflexivity.

point $(b, a) \in S$. The set of all solid points for which this is true constitutes a symmetric relation $R$ on $S$. On the other hand, the figure obviously would remain an example of a symmetric relation were some of the points on the diagonal to be filled in. Notice that the relation actually depicted is neither reflexive nor transitive. The reader may enjoy sketching for himself the graph of a relation that is transitive (but not symmetric, nor reflexive), though he is cautioned that the situation here is by no means so simple and obvious as in the two previous illustrations. The following hint may be of some help. The definition of transitivity may be satisfied *vacuously*. That is to say, the definition says that $R$ is transitive whenever *if $a$ $R$ $b$ and $b$ $R$ $c$ then $a$ $R$ $c$*, and this if-then statement remains true (vacuously) when the "if" part is false. Thus, for example, the relation "is a husband of" is (vacuously) transitive, for *if $a$ $H$ $b$ and $b$ $H$ $c$* (impossible, for $b$ must be a woman) then, indeed, $a$ $H$ $c$.

Additional insight may be gained by investigating relations that are reflexive and transitive but not symmetric, reflexive and symmetric but not transitive, and symmetric and transitive but not reflexive. As regards the last example, we bring out that fact that: if $R$ is a relation on $S$ that is symmetric and transitive, *and if for each $x \in S$ there is some $y \in S$ such that $x$ $R$ $y$*, then $R$ is reflexive (see Exercise 13). Such a relation is of a rather special type, which we now proceed to discuss.

### 4.3.4 Equivalence Relations and Partitions

We begin this section with a definition. Let $R$ be a relation on $S$. Then $R$ is said to be an *equivalence relation* if, and only if:

(1) $x$ $R$ $x$, for all $x \in S$;

(2) whenever $x$ $R$ $y$, then $y$ $R$ $x$, for all $x, y \in S$;

(3) whenever $x$ $R$ $y$ and $y$ $R$ $z$, then $x$ $R$ $z$ for all $x, y, z \in S$.

Thus, $R$ is an equivalence relation whenever $R$ is reflexive, symmetric, and transitive.

Equivalence relations play an extremely important role in mathematics; possibly the most common example of an equivalence relation is the relation of equality. The relations of similarity and congruence on a set of triangles, and the relation of being parallel on a set of lines in a plane,* are other examples of equivalence relations. Additional examples are the relations "is contemporary with," "was born in the same state as," and so on. (The reader should satisfy himself that these are all equivalence relations by showing that properties (1)–(3) above are satisfied.)

The reason for the name equivalence relation should be apparent. All

---

* We assume that a line may be regarded as being parallel to itself.

congruent triangles, for example, are "equivalent" in a certain sense, though they may look rather different in their spatial orientation; all females are "equivalent" in the sense of belonging to the same sex. Indeed, given a mixed set of people, $P$, we may easily partition the set into a set, $F$, of females and a set, $M$, of males. Notice that $F \cap M = \mathfrak{E}$ and $F \cup M = P$. This brings out a very important and useful property of equivalence relations in general. An equivalence relation $R$ on a set $S$ may be used to *partition* $S$ into a set of mutually exclusive subsets in such a way that every $x \in S$ is in at least one of these subsets. (That it is in *at most* one of these subsets follows from their being mutually exclusive—that is, the intersection of any pair of these subsets is empty.) A common example is the partitioning of the integers into even and odd integers.

Somewhat more formally: Given an equivalence relation $R$ on a set $S$, then a partition of $S$ is a collection of subsets of $S$ such that:

(1) if $x$ and $y$ are in the same subset, then $x \, R \, y$;

(2) every $x \in S$ is in at least one of the subsets;

(3) every two distinct subsets are disjoint;

(4) if $x$ and $y$ are in different subsets, then neither $x \, R \, y$ nor $y \, R \, x$.

The collection of subsets satisfying conditions (1)–(4) above are called *equivalence classes;* all the elements in any particular set ("class") are equivalent to each other.

Consider, now, the relation "$x$ differs from $y$ by a multiple of (say) 3" on the set of positive integers, $P$. This is an equivalence relation as the following considerations show. Let $R$ stand for this relation. Then $x \, R \, x$, if we concede that $0 \times 3 = 0$ is a multiple of 3 (which it certainly is). Furthermore, if $x \, R \, y$, then $y \, R \, x$ (for example, if $15 - 9 = 2 \times 3$—that is, 15 differs from 9 by a multiple of 3—then, also, $9 - 15 = -2 \times 3$—that is, 9 differs from 15 by a multiple of 3). Finally, if $x \, R \, y$ and $y \, R \, z$, then, evidently, $x \, R \, z$ as well. This relation may now be used to partition the set of positive integers, $S = \{1, 2, 3, \ldots\}$, into equivalence classes, as follows. For any $x \in S$, the set of all $x_i \in S$ for which $x_i \, R \, x$ will be an *equivalence class generated by* $x$. Thus, let us start with 1: then $4 \, R \, 1$ (because $4 - 1 = 3$ is a multiple of 3), and $7 \, R \, 1$ (because $7 - 1 = 6$ is a multiple of 3); continuing in this way the equivalence class $\{1, 4, 7, 10, \ldots\}$ is generated by 1. Similarly, $2 \in S$ generates the equivalence class $\{2, 5, 8, 11, \ldots\}$ and $3 \in S$ generates $\{3, 6, 9, 12, \ldots\}$. Evidently, we come to an end here, for 4 generates the same equivalence class as 1 (since 4 and 1 are equivalent), 5 generates the same class as 2, 6 the same as 3, 7 the same as 1 again, and so on. Thus, the following collection of these subsets of $S$ forms a partition $\mathfrak{P}$, of $S$:

$$\mathfrak{P} = \{\{1, 4, 7, 10, \ldots\}, \{2, 5, 8, 11, \ldots\}, \{3, 6, 9, 12, \ldots\}\}.$$

Such a set (collection) of equivalence classes (sets) is often denoted by $P/R$ and is called the *quotient set*.

Notice that the intersection of any two of the (sub)sets in this collection is empty and the union of all three is $S$ itself. Furthermore, notice that only if $x$ and $y$ are in the *same* class (set), then $x \, R \, y$—that is, $x$ and $y$ differ from each other by a multiple of 3; and if $x$ and $y$ come from different classes (sets), then neither $x \, R \, y$ nor $y \, R \, x$. Such elements are said to be *incomparable* under the relation $R$.

A set may be partitioned by an equivalence relation in a number of different ways. For example, given a set, $\{a, b, c\}$, containing three elements, it may happen that the three elements are all equivalent to each other. This yields the partition

$$\mathfrak{P} = \{\{a, b, c\}\}.$$

Alternatively, it may happen that only $b$ and $c$ are equivalent to each other and $a$ is equivalent to itself, in which case

$$\mathfrak{P} = \{\{a\}, \{b, c\}\}.$$

The remaining possible partitions are

$$\{\{b\}, \{a, c\}\}; \quad \{\{c\}, \{a, b\}\}; \quad \{\{a\}, \{b\}, \{c\}\}.$$

The number of possible partitions rises fairly rapidly with the number of elements in the set. For example, a set of 4 elements may be partitioned in 15 different possible ways, while the number of possible partitions on a set of 5 elements is 52, and the number of possible partitions on a set of 6 elements is already 203.

## 4.4 Order

As mentioned previously, we may consider certain special transitive relations having either one of the remaining two properties of reflexivity or symmetry. Such relations are called *ordering relations* and, among these, possibly the most primitive is the *quasi-ordering relation*.

A relation $R$ on a set $S$ that is reflexive and transitive is called a *quasi-ordering* relation. The relation is called "quasi" because there may exist pairs of distinct elements in $S$ for which *neither $x \, R \, y$ nor $y \, R \, x$* holds. Such elements are incomparable. Furthermore, *both $x \, R \, y$ and $y \, R \, x$* are *not* excluded. However, the relation is not necessarily symmetric, for we do *not* claim that $x \, R \, y$ implies $y \, R \, x$.

If $R$ is a quasi-ordering relation and we have $x \, R \, y$, it means, roughly, that $x$ is at least as far along in the order as $y$. Some examples of quasi-ordering relations are: "is at least as probable as" on a set of events, "is at least as old as" on a set of people, "is liked at least as well as" on, say, a set of desirable objects, "implies" on a set of statements, and "includes" on a collection of subsets of a given set. The reader should satisfy himself that each of these relations is indeed reflexive and transitive.

Take "implies," for example. Every statement obviously (trivially) implies itself; and if one statement implies a second while the second implies a third, then the first obviously implies the third as well. Furthermore, the relation is obviously not symmetric, for if one statement implies a second, this does not mean that the second must imply the first, as well; it *may*, of course, but in that case the statements are said to be equivalent. Neither is this relation asymmetric, for the fact that one statement implies a second does not mean that it is logically impossible for the second to imply the first, as well. Finally, it is rather easy to make up a set of statements containing pairs of statements neither of which implies the other—that is, incomparable statements.

There is an interesting difference between a quasi-ordering relation such as "is at least as old as" and "includes." In the case of the first relation, there will be no incomparable elements; that is, if $P$ is a set of people, and $R =$ "is at least as old as" is a relation on $P$, then for any $x, y \in P$ we will always have $x \, R \, y$ or $y \, R \, x$. Such a situation is described by saying that $R$ is *connected* on $P$. That this is not the case for the relation "implies," on an arbitrary set of statements, was already mentioned. That it is not the case for inclusion applied to a collection of subsets of a given set is easy to show by example. Let $S = \{a, b, c\}$; then $\{a, b\}$ and $\{a, c\}$ are incomparable, since neither $\{a, b\} \subseteq \{a, c\}$ nor $\{a, c\} \subseteq \{a, b\}$ holds. Thus, neither implication nor inclusion is connected. We are now in a position to define another kind of order.

A quasi-ordering relation, $R$, on a set $S$, is said to be a *weak ordering* relation whenever it is connected. Alternatively, we may define a weak ordering relation as one that is connected (which implies that it is also reflexive) and transitive. The relation $\leqslant$ (less than or equal to) on a set of real numbers is typical of a weak ordering relation. Notice that for any (every) pair of numbers $x$ and $y$ we can *always* say either $x \leqslant y$ or $y \leqslant x$ (or, possibly, both). Notice, especially, that $x$ and $y$ need not be distinct; that is, even $x \leqslant x$ holds. The relation "is at least as tall as" on a set of people is another example of a weak ordering relation.

The relation $\leqslant$ has an additional interesting property. Whenever we have both $x \leqslant y$ and $y \leqslant x$, we conclude that $x = y$. That is to say, this relation is antisymmetric. Such a situation is characterized by referring to $\leqslant$ as a *partial ordering*. More precisely, a quasi-ordering whose equivalence relation is the identity ("equality") is called a *partial ordering* relation. Evidently, the relation "is at least as old as" is not a partial ordering, for—calling this relation $R$—the fact that $x \, R \, y$ and $y \, R \, x$ does not imply that $x = y$ (that is, that $x$ and $y$ are identical); though, of course, they may be regarded as "equivalent" in the sense of being of the same age. The relation "$x$ divides $y$" (exactly) on the set of natural numbers is another example of a partial ordering relation. A *connected* partial ordering is often called a *simple ordering*.

The relation $\leqslant$ (less than or equal to), say, on the set of rational numbers, is an example of a simple ordering; it is, moreover, a compound relation (recall that relations are *sets* and therefore unions and intersections of relations are also relations), being made up of $<$ (is less than) and $=$ (is equal to). The relation $=$ has already been pointed out as an example of an equivalence relation. The relation $<$ serves to introduce the final type of ordering relation to be considered in this section. Possibly the most obvious thing one remembers about $<$, as defined on a set of real numbers in elementary algebra, is that it is asymmetric. That is to say, if one real number is less than a second, then it follows that the second is *not* less than the first. (It is, in fact, *greater*.) Evidently, $<$ is also a transitive relation. This leads to the following definition.

A connected relation that is asymmetric and transitive is called a *strong ordering* relation. Nothing is said regarding reflexivity, since it is easy to show that a relation that is asymmetric is also irreflexive. The reader is cautioned, however, that a strong ordering relation is not simply one that is transitive and irreflexive, for an irreflexive relation need not be asymmetric.

In fact, a relation that is irreflexive and transitive is sometimes called a *preference relation*. The reason for this is fairly obvious, for if $P$ stands for "is preferred to," $x\,P\,x$ is evidently nonsense: one cannot *prefer* something to itself. Notice, however, that if on one occasion one prefers $x$ over $y$ *and* on another occasion one prefers $y$ over $x$, it would be reasonable to conclude that one is *indifferent* between $x$ and $y$.

One may, moreover, characterize a strong ordering relation as follows. Let $R$ be a relation on $S$. Then $R$ is said to be a *strong ordering* relation if:

(i) for all $x \in S$, not-($x\,R\,x$);

(ii) for all $x, y \in S$, if $x \neq y$, then $x\,R\,y$ or $y\,R\,x$; and

(iii) for all $x, y, z \in S$, if $x\,R\,y$ and $y\,R\,z$, then $x\,R\,z$.

Incidentally, relations fulfilling these three conditions are also often called *linear orderings*. Relations such as "is taller than" on a set of people and "is earlier than" on a set of instants are evidently strong orderings. Notice, however, that a relation such as "is the ancestor of" on a set of people is *not* a strong ordering; for it is not true that, given any two distinct individuals (that is, if $x \neq y$), one must be the ancestor of the other.

In closing this section, we mention two additional schemes that are sometimes useful for studying relations.

| $R$ | $a$ | $b$ | $c$ |
|-----|-----|-----|-----|
| $a$ | 1 | 0 | 0 |
| $b$ | 0 | 1 | 0 |
| $c$ | 0 | 0 | 1 |

(a)

| $R$ | $a$ | $b$ | $c$ |
|-----|-----|-----|-----|
| $a$ | 0 | 1 | 1 |
| $b$ | 0 | 0 | 1 |
| $c$ | 0 | 0 | 0 |

(b)

**Figure 12.** The matrix of a relation. (a) A reflexive
relation. (b) A transitive relation.

One scheme is quite similar to the graphing technique considered
previously. It consists in letting the elements of $A \times B$ (where $A$ need not
be distinct from $B$) represent the rows and columns of a table. If an element
$a \in A$ is related to an element $b \in B$—that is, if $a\ R\ b$—then the number "1"
instead of a solid circle (as in the graphing technique) is placed at the
intersection of column $a$ and row $b$ of the table; otherwise this cell of the
table is filled with a zero (instead of an open circle). Notice that the entire
table represents $A \times B$ and only the pattern of 1's represents $R$.

The table shown in Figure 12(a) is an example of a reflexive relation $R$
on a set $A = \{a, b, c\}$. Notice that the table contains 1's along the main
diagonal and 0's everywhere else. Figure 12(b) is an example of a transitive
relation on $A$. Such tables are commonly called *matrices*—matrices will be
discussed further in the next chapter. Incidentally, one may associate little
vector diagrams with such matrices. Figures 13(a) and (b) show the diagrams
associated with the matrices of Figures 12(a) and (b), respectively. Such
diagrams are often called *oriented graphs* and will be discussed further in the
next chapter. The rule is simple. The elements comprising the set are
arbitrarily attached as labels to points in the plane and an arrow is drawn
*from* a point $x$ *to* a point $y$ if, and only if, $x\ R\ y$; if $y\ R\ x$, the arrow is drawn
in the reverse direction; and, of course, if $x\ R\ y$ and $y\ R\ x$, a double-headed
arrow is drawn between the points labeled $x$ and $y$.

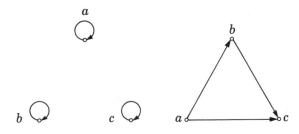

**Figure 13.** The digraph of a relation. (a) A reflexive
relation. (b) A transitive relation.

The second scheme is similar to the one just discussed except that arrows, or directed lines, are not used. This scheme is best explained using an illustration. In Figure 14 we show the collection of all subsets of a given set $S = \{a, b, c\}$, including $S$ itself and the null set $\mathfrak{E}$, arranged in a certain way. The arrangement is obtained as follows. If $A \subseteq B$, where $A$ and $B$ are any two sets from the collection of subsets of $S$, then $A$ is placed below $B$ and the two are connected by a line. Observe that under this agreement the use of arrows would add nothing to the diagram. (Such diagrams are called *ordinary* or *linear graphs*—see the next chapter.) Another convention about the way this diagram is drawn is extremely important. Notice that not all

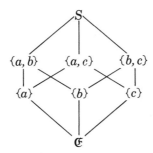

**Figure 14.** The set of all subsets of $S = \{a, b, c\}$ ordered by $\subseteq$.

the possible lines have been used in making the diagram. Thus, $\mathfrak{E}$ is a subset of, say, $\{a, b\}$ and, while it is placed below $\{a, b\}$, there is no line connecting it to $\mathfrak{E}$. In fact, there should be a line from $\mathfrak{E}$ to every one of the other sets shown in the diagram. These extra lines have been omitted by the following very reasonable agreement. There *is* a line from $\mathfrak{E}$ to $\{a\}$ and one from $\{a\}$ to $\{a, b\}$. By transitivity, we know that there must also be a line from $\mathfrak{E}$ to $\{a, b\}$ and so there is no need to draw it in. Such a convention results in a greatly simplified figure. Thus, whenever we have $A \subseteq B$, for any arbitrary pair of sets in a collection, although we do not necessarily have a direct line connecting $A$ and $B$, there will always be some *path* of lines going up from $A$ to $B$. Notice that the omission of certain other lines on the diagram is essential: the omission of a line between $\{a, c\}$ and $\{b\}$ and the omission of lines from between elements (sets) in the same row. The omission of these lines signifies that these sets are incomparable.

In summary, we repeat the principal definitions and types of orders considered in this section.

A relation $R$, on a set $S$, that is transitive and reflexive is called a *quasi-ordering* relation. That is, if $R$ is a *quasi-ordering* on $S$, then: (i) $x\,R\,x$ for all $x \in S$; and (ii) if $x\,R\,y$ and $y\,R\,z$ then $x\,R\,z$ for all $x, y, z \in S$.

*Examples:* implication and set inclusion.

If $R$ is a relation on $S$ and if, for every $x, y \in S$, we have either $x \, R \, y$ or $y \, R \, x$ (or both), then $R$ is *connected*.

A connected quasi-ordering relation is called a *weak ordering*.

*Example:* "is as tall as," on a set of people.

A quasi-ordering whose equivalence relation is the identity is called a *partial ordering*.

*Example:* $\subseteq$ (set inclusion).

A connected partial ordering is called a *simple ordering*.

*Example:* $\leqslant$ ("is less than or equal to," on a set of real numbers).

A connected relation that is asymmetric (and thus irreflexive) and transitive is called a *strong* (or *linear*) *ordering* relation.

*Examples:* $<$ or $>$ ("is earlier than," "is less than," or "later than," "is greater than").

## 4.5   Mapping and Functions

Let $A$ and $B$ be any two arbitrary sets. A *rule of correspondence* $F$ that assigns to each element $a \in A$ (read: "$a$ in $A$") an element $b \in B$ is called a *mapping* of $A$ *into* $B$, symbolized, $F : A \to B$. The unique element $b \in B$ that corresponds to $a \in A$ is called the *image* of $a$. If more than one element in $A$ is assigned to a unique correspondent $b \in B$, the mapping is said to be *many-one;* if a single element $a \in A$ has more than a single correspondent $b \in B$, the mapping is said to be *one-many;* finally, if one, and only one, element $a \in A$ corresponds to one, and only one, element $b \in B$, the mapping is said to be *one-to-one*, or *one-one*. Often $b = F(a)$, or $b = Fa$, is written to indicate the association between elements $a \in A$ and $b \in B$; when written in this form, and as long as the mapping is not one-many, it is customary to speak of $b$ as a *function* of $a$. In more advanced works, the notation $F : A \to B$ is the preferred one and, indeed, the terms "mapping" and "function" are often used interchangeably—particularly when the mapping is from a set of numbers to a set of numbers. If *every* $b \in B$ is the image of some (one or more) element $a \in A$, the mapping is said to be *onto* and we speak of a mapping of $A$ onto $B$. If there is at least one element in $B$ that is not an image-element, the mapping is said to be *into*. Otherwise it is called, simply, *on* or is said to be from $A$ to $B$.

It is important to note that $F$ consists of *ordered couples* of the type $(a, f(a))$; that is, $F \subseteq A \times B$, and $F$ is therefore a *binary relation*. It will be recalled that a binary relation from $A$ to $B$ is simply a subset $C$ of ordered couples in $A \times B$. (Notice that each $a \in A$ must thus be accounted for.) Thus, a function is simply a special kind of relation or set of ordered couples.

Incidentally, it is now a simple matter to define equivalence between sets. We will say that the set $A$ is *equivalent* to the set $B$, symbolized $A \simeq B$, whenever $A$ can be mapped *one-to-one onto* $B$. The reader may satisfy himself that the symbol "$\sim$", defined in this way, represents an equivalence relation: that is, it is transitive, symmetric, and reflexive. An analogous relation between *ordered* sets is the relation of *similarity*. This is an equivalence relation between ordered sets and may be defined as follows: An ordered set $A$ will be said to be *similar* to an ordered set $B$, symbolized $A \sim B$, if there is a mapping $f: A \to B$ that is one-one onto and such that, for any elements $a \in A$ and $a' \in A$, $a\ R\ a'$ if, and only if, $f(a)\ R f(a')$. In other words, two ordered sets are said to be similar if there exists a one-to-one correspondence between their elements that preserves the order relation.

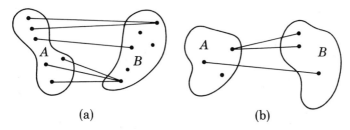

**Figure 15.** (a) The function $F$. (b) A relation that is not
a function.

To return to our previous discussion, as we have just seen, a function is a binary relation that couples every element in the domain of the relation to a unique (that is, one and only one) element in its range. And, if $F$ is a relation from $A$ to $B$, we will say that $F$ is a *functional relation*, or *function from $A$ to $B$*, just in case whenever $(a, b) \in F$ and $(a, c) \in F$ then $b = c$. In other words, the relation $F$ is said to be a function *only* if different ordered pairs in $F$ always have different first elements; that is, each $a \in A$ appears as first element in one and only one ordered pair belonging to $F$. (Notice that *each* $a \in A$ must thus be accounted for.) Figure 15(a) presents an example of a function. Notice that the mapping is *into* the set $B$ (that is, there are elements in $B$ that are not the images of any elements in $A$), and that every element in $A$ is accounted for. The relation depicted in Figure 15(b) fails to be a function for two reasons (either one of which alone would disqualify it from being a function): there is an element in $A$ (namely, $a_1$) that has two images in $B$ ($b_1$ and $b_2$); there is an element in $A$ that has no correspondent in $B$ ($a_2$).

Finally, suppose we are given a set* $\mathfrak{D}$ and a rule $F$ that assign some "object" to every element of $\mathfrak{D}$. Then $F$ is called a *function on* $\mathfrak{D}$. If $x$ is any element of $\mathfrak{D}$, we denote the object $y$ assigned to $x$ (under $F$) by $F(x)$ and call

---

* We use the German script $\mathfrak{D}$ and $\mathfrak{R}$ in this discussion to emphasize the special nature of these sets.

it the *value* of $F$ at $x$. This object may, itself, be an element of $\mathfrak{D}$, but it need not be. Furthermore, the various objects so assigned may be all different, all the same, or any kind of mixture. The set is called the *domain* of the function, and the set $\mathfrak{R}$ of all objects $F(x)$ that are used in the assignment is called the *range* of $F$ (see Figure 16). The sets $\mathfrak{D}$ and $\mathfrak{R}$ may be quite arbitrary, the only restrictions being that $F$ assign a unique (one, and only one) element of $\mathfrak{R}$ to each element of $\mathfrak{D}$.

The correspondence, or "associations," between the elements of the two sets $\mathfrak{D}$ and $\mathfrak{R}$, as given by the mapping $F: \mathfrak{D} \to \mathfrak{R}$, is *from* an element $x \in \mathfrak{D}$ *to* an element $f(x) = y \in \mathfrak{R}$. It is often useful to consider the mapping obtained by reversing the correspondence. For each element $y \in \mathfrak{R}$ we may

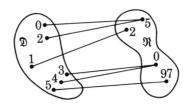

**Figure 16.** The domain and range of a function.

define the *inverse image* of $y$ under $F$, denoted by $F^{-1}(y)$ or $F^{-1}y$, to be the set of all elements of $\mathfrak{D}$ that correspond to $y$—that is,

$$F^{-1}(y) = \{x \mid x \in \mathfrak{D} \text{ and } f(x) = y\}.$$

Given the mapping $F: \mathfrak{D} \to \mathfrak{R}$, the mapping $F^{-1}: \mathfrak{R} \to \mathfrak{D}$ is called the *inverse* mapping. Notice that if $F: A \to B$ is a function, then $F^{-1}: B \to A$ need *not*, in general, also be a function. It may happen that $F^{-1}(y)$ for a single element $y \in B$ may consist of more than one element of $A$. Figure 15 is an example of a mapping whose *inverse* mapping is *not* a *function*. However, whenever a function, $F: A \to B$, is a one-one mapping onto, the inverse mapping, $F^{-1}: B \to A$, will also be a function called the *inverse function*.

Let us consider some examples of mappings that are functions.

1. Let $\mathfrak{D} = \{0, 1, 2, 3, 4, 5\}$ and let $f(0) = 5$, $f(1) = 2$, $f(2) = 5$, $f(3) = 0$, $f(4) = 0$, $f(5) = 97$. This function is shown in Figure 16; its range is $\{0, 2, 5, 97\}$. This function has no inverse; that is, the inverse mapping is not a function.

2. Let $R$ be the set of all real numbers, and let $X \subseteq R$ and $Y \subseteq R$ be two, not necessarily distinct (that is, we do not exclude the possibility that $X = Y$), subsets of $R$. Then the mapping $F: X \to Y$ such that $y = F(x) = x + 1$, where $x \in X$ and $y = F(x) \in Y$, is a function. We have here: $F = \{(x, y) \mid y = x + 1\}$. The reader may find it useful to make a rough sketch

similar to Figure 16. Some of the elements in the domain of $F$ are, for example: $0, 1, \sqrt{2}, -1, \ldots$ ; the images of these are the elements $1, 2,$ $\sqrt{2} + 1, 0, \ldots$, respectively, to be found in the range of $F$. Notice that this mapping is *onto*. The inverse function $F^{-1}(y) = y - 1$.

3. Let $X$ and $Y$ be sets of real numbers as above, and consider the mapping $G: X \to Y$, where $G(x) = x^2$. This says that to every $x \in X$ we make correspond $x^2 \in Y$—that is, $x^2$ is the image of $x$. Thus, $G = \{(x, y) \mid y = x^2\}$. Notice that this function is a mapping of $X$ *into* $Y$ because there are a good many elements (an infinite number, in fact) in $Y$ that are not in the range of $G$; for example, none of the negative numbers in $Y$ is in the range of $G$. Notice, furthermore, that the inverse mapping $G: Y \to X$ is *not* a function. For one thing, the inverse image is not unique—that is, the inverse image of $1, G^{-1}(1)$, is $1$ or $-1$; furthermore, no negative numbers have inverses—for example, $G^{-1}(-1) = \mathfrak{E}$.

4. Let $\mathfrak{D} \subseteq N$, where $N = \{x \mid x$ is rational and $0 < x < 1\}$, and suppose $F(x) = 1/x$, for all $x \in \mathfrak{D}$. The range, $\mathfrak{R}$, of $F$ will again be a set of rational numbers, but only those that are greater than $1$; i.e., $\mathfrak{R} = \{y \mid y$ is rational and $y > 1\}$.

5. Let $\mathfrak{D}$ be any arbitrary set whatsoever, and let $F(x) = x$ for every $x \in \mathfrak{D}$. The range of $F$ is obviously $\mathfrak{D}$ itself. This function is called the *identity function*.

6. As our final example, let $\mathfrak{D}$ be any set whatsoever, and let $F(x) = a$, where $a$ is some fixed object, for each $x \in \mathfrak{D}$. Then the range of $F$ is the set $\{a\}$, consisting of a single element, and $F$ is called a *constant function*.

In summary, and somewhat more formally, a *function* is a triplet $(F, A, B)$ consisting of two sets $A$ and $B$ and a set (relation) $F$ included in $A \times B$ such that no element $a \in A$ is the first element of two distinct couples, $(a, b)$ and $(a, c)$, in $F$. In particular, if $\mathfrak{D} \subseteq A$—consisting of the elements $x \in A$ that are the first elements of pairs $(x, y) \in F$—then the *function* $(F, A, B)$ will be denoted by $F: \mathfrak{D} \to \mathfrak{R}$, where $\mathfrak{R} \subseteq B$. The set $\mathfrak{D}$ is called the *domain* of $F$ and the set of elements $y \in B$, which are second elements of some pair $(a, b) \in F$, is called the *range*, $\mathfrak{R}$, of $F$. If $(x, y) \in F$, then we will use the notation $y = F(x)$ and call $y$ the *image* of $x$ under $F$. Evidently, if for each $x \in \mathfrak{D}$, $f(x) \in \mathfrak{R} \subseteq B$ is given, then the function $F: \mathfrak{D} \to \mathfrak{R}$ is uniquely determined. While every member of $\mathfrak{D}$ must have an image, furthermore, an element in $\mathfrak{R}$ can be the image of several elements in $\mathfrak{D}$. Finally, the subset $F \subseteq A \times B$ consisting of all ordered pairs $(x, f(x)) \in F$ may be exhibited in a scheme called the *graph of* $F$. For example, the graph of the *function* $F = \{(1, a), (2, c), (3, b), (4, b)\}$ is shown in Figure 17(a). Notice that, although Figure 17(b) is the graph of a *relation*, it cannot be the graph

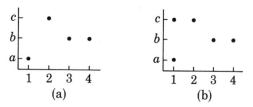

**Figure 17.** Comparison of a function and a relation.
(a) Graph of a function with $\mathfrak{D} = \{1, 2, 3, 4\}$ and $\mathfrak{R} = \{a, b, c\}$. (b) Graph of a relation with $\mathfrak{D} = \{1, 2, 3, 4\}$ and $\mathfrak{R} = \{a, b, c\}$.

of any function, by our definition, since 1 has two distinct images, $a$ and $c$. The notion of a relation, and of a mapping, is thus *less* restrictive than that of a function.

We conclude this section with a brief discussion of the important notion of an *operation on a set*. We begin with a definition: Let $S$ be any set; then by an *operation on $S$* is meant a function from $S \times S$ to $S$. Such an operation is commonly referred to as a *binary operation*, for obvious reasons.

For example, let $S = \{a, b\}$. To construct an operation on $S$ we have only to assign to each element of $S \times S$ an element of $S$. We may effect such a correspondence in a perfectly arbitrary way; for example:

$$(a, a) \rightarrow a; \qquad (b, a) \rightarrow b;$$

$$(a, b) \rightarrow a; \qquad (b, b) \rightarrow a.$$

Let us call this operation the "star" ($*$) operation, to give it a name. Then we may write

$$a * a = a; \qquad b * a = b;$$

$$a * b = a; \qquad b * b = a.$$

Alternatively, the effects of the operation may be displayed in the form of a "multiplication" table as shown below. Notice the way the star table must be read and that $a * b = a$ while $b * a = b$. Thus, this operation is not commutative; that is, $a * b \neq b * a$. The familiar operations of multiplication and addition are examples of operations that *are* commutative, since $a \cdot b = b \cdot a$ and $a + b = b + a$ when ($\cdot$) and ($+$) are defined in the customary way on, say, the set of all real numbers. This remains true when ($\cdot$) and ($+$) are defined as Boolean operations on a set of statements (in which case ($\cdot$) may be interpreted as "and" and ($+$) may be interpreted as "or"). Finally, notice that star is not even associative, for

$$b * (a * b) = b * a \quad (\text{since } a * b = a) \quad = b$$

while

$$(b * a) * b = b * b \quad (\text{since } b * a = b) \quad = a.$$

| * | a | b |
|---|---|---|
| a | a | a |
| b | b | a |

Again, ordinary multiplication and addition are, of course, associative.

The table below, which is the table for, say, a dot ($\cdot$) operation, is an example of an operation that is both commutative and associative. In this

| $\cdot$ | a | b |
|---|---|---|
| a | a | b |
| b | b | a |

respect it is similar to ordinary multiplication. Also, notice that $a$ functions as a unity element here in that $a \cdot a = a$ and $a \cdot b = b \cdot a = b$. (This is in analogy to the case with numbers where $1 \cdot 1 = 1$ and $1 \cdot x = x \cdot 1 = x$.) However, the operation also differs markedly from ordinary multiplication in that $b \cdot b = a$ (rather than $b^2$).

We repeat Table 3.5 of the previous chapter in the present form so that it may be contrasted with the table just displayed above. The operation $+$ is also commutative and associative and, here, $b$ functions as a unity or identity element, since $b + b = b$ and $a + b = b + a = a$. (This is in analogy to the case with numbers where 0 is the identity under addition.)

| + | a | b |
|---|---|---|
| a | a | a |
| b | a | b |

As you already know, this little system is capable of an interpretation wherein $+$ is Boolean addition with $a = 1$ and $b = 0$. But other interpretations are possible. For example, let $a = 0$, $b = 1$, and let $+$ be interpreted as ordinary multiplication, then this little table represents the usual situation. Alternatively, let $a =$ an even integer, $b =$ an odd integer, and let $+$ represent ordinary multiplication, then the table represents the usual situation wherein the product of a pair of numbers is even when either factor is even and odd otherwise.

The previous table above is also capable of a number of interpretations. For example, the dot operation may be interpreted as logical equivalence with $a =$ true and $b =$ false. Then, since a pair of statements are logically equivalent only if both are simultaneously true or both are simultaneously false (that is, one statement cannot be equivalent to another if one is false whenever the other is true, or vice versa) the table, with this interpretation, correctly depicts the situation. Alternatively, let $a$ represent an even integer and let $b$ represent an odd integer and let the dot operation stand for ordinary addition. Again, let $a = +1$, $b = -1$, and let the dot be ordinary multiplication.

If there is a special element $e$ such that for every element $a \in A$ we have

$$e * a = a * e = a,$$

then $e$ is called the *identity element* with respect to the operation $*$. For example, $a$ is an identity element with respect to the dot operation above because

$$a \cdot b = b \cdot a = b$$

and

$$a \cdot a = a.$$

As a more common example, let $\varphi \colon R \times R \to R$ be the operation of addition on the set $R$ of real numbers. Then 0 is the identity element for addition, since for every real number $a \in R$

$$0 * a = a * 0 = a,$$

where $*$ is interpreted as ordinary addition of real numbers. Alternatively, 1 is the identity for multiplication, since

$$1 * a = a * 1 = a$$

when $a \in R$ and $*$ is interpreted as ordinary multiplicationn of real numbers.

As another example, the universal set $\mathfrak{U}$ is an identity element under the operation of intersection, since for every $A \subseteq \mathfrak{U}$ we have

$$A * \mathfrak{U} = \mathfrak{U} * A = A$$

when $*$ is interpreted as $\cap$.

Let $\varphi \colon A \times A \to A$ be an operation written $\varphi(a, b) = a * b$ and let $e \in A$ be the identity element for $\varphi$. It may happen that there is a special element in $A$, which we will denote $a^{-1}$, such that

$$a^{-1} * a = a * a^{-1} = e.$$

When this is the case, the element $a^{-1} \in A$ is called the *inverse* of the element $a \in A$. For example, $1/x$ is the inverse of $x \in R$ under ordinary multiplication. Again, if $a \in I$, where $I$ is the set of integers, then $-a$ is the inverse of $a$ under addition, since

$$-a * a = a * -a = 0$$

when $*$ is interpreted as ordinary addition.

We introduce one more notion pertaining to operations. If $\varphi \colon A \times A \to A$ is an operation and $B \subseteq A$, then $B$ is said to be *closed* under the operation of $\varphi$ if

$$\varphi(B \times B) \subseteq B.$$

—in other words, whenever (for every $x, y \in B$) we have $\varphi(x, y) \in B$. For example, the operations of addition and multiplication on the set of natural numbers are both closed. Again, the set of even numbers is closed under addition, since the sum of a pair of even numbers is also an even number. But the set of odd numbers is not closed under addition, since the sum of a pair of odd numbers is not an odd number.

## 4.6 Summary

The *product set* $A \times B$ of two sets $A$ and $B$ is defined to be the collection of all *ordered pairs* $(a, b)$, in that order, such that $a \in A$ and $b \in B$—that is,

$$A \times B = \{(a, b) \mid a \in A \text{ and } b \in B\}.$$

An ordered pair $(a, b)$ is said to be identical to an ordered pair $(c, d)$ if, and only if, $a = c$ and $b = d$. Thus, in general, $(a, b) \neq (b, a)$.

More generally,

$$\prod_{i=1}^{n} A_i = A_1 \times A_2 \times \cdots \times A_n$$

is defined to be the collection of *n-tuples* $(a_1, a_2, \ldots, a_n)$ such that the $i$th *component*, $a_i$, is an element of the $i$th set $A_i$.

A *binary relation* $R$ is defined to be a subset of some product set $A \times B$ (where $B$ need not be different from $A$). A relation is thus a set of ordered pairs. If an ordered pair $(a, b)$ belongs to a relation $R$, we may write $(a, b) \in R$ or, equivalently, $a \, R \, b$ (signifying that $a$ is related to $b$). Since relations are sets, the techniques of set theory may be used in their study.

If

$$R = \{(a, b) \mid a \in A \text{ and } b \in B\},$$

then $A$ is called the *domain* of $R$, $\mathfrak{D}(R)$, and $B$ is called the *range* (or *counter domain*), $\mathfrak{R}(R)$. The field, $\mathfrak{F}(R)$, of a relation is the union of its domain with its range.

If $a \, R \, b$, then the relation $R$, such that $b \, R' \, a$, is called the *converse* of $R$. The following properties of relations were defined:

1. If $R$ is a relation on $S$ and $x \, R \, x$ for all $x \in S$, $R$ is said to be *reflexive*; if $x \, R \, x$ for some $x \in S$, it is said to be *nonreflexive* (or *mesoreflexive*); finally, if $x \, R \, x$ for no $x \in S$, $R$ is said to be *irreflexive*.

2. If $R$ is a relation on $S$, where $x, y \in S$, and $x \, R \, y$ implies $y \, R \, x$, $R$ is said to be *symmetric*; if $x \, R \, y$ does not imply $y \, R \, x$, $R$ is said to be *nonsymmetric* (or *mesosymmetric*); finally, if $x \, R \, y$ implies that $y \, R \, x$ does not hold, then $R$ is called *asymmetric*. In addition, if $x \, R \, y$ and $y \, R \, x$ imply $x = y$, the relation is called *antisymmetric*.

3. Given $R$ a relation on $S$, where $x, y, z \in S$. If $x \, R \, y$ and $y \, R \, z$ imply $x \, R \, z$, then $R$ is said to be a *transitive* relation; if $x \, R \, y$ and $y \, R \, z$ imply that $x \, R \, z$ does not hold, $R$ is said to be *intransitive*; finally, a relation $R$ that is transitive for some elements in $S$ is called *nontransitive* (or *mesotransitive*).

A relation that is reflexive, symmetric, and transitive is called an *equivalence relation*. An equivalence relation $E$ on a set $S$ may be used to *partition* $S$ into a set of mutually exclusive subsets $S_1, S_2, \ldots, S_n$ in such a way that $S_1 \cup S_2 \cup \cdots \cup S_n = S$. The elements belonging to any particular $S_i$ are said to be equivalent to each other, while no element in $S_i$ is equivalent to any element in $S_j$, for all $i \neq j$. In other words, if $x$ and $y$ are any two elements in the same $S_i$, then $x \, E \, y$; otherwise, $x \, \not\!E \, y$ (where $\not\!E$ means not-$E$). For any $x \in S$, the set of all $x_i \in S$ for which $x_i \, E \, x$ is called an *equivalence class generated by* $x$ . A partition is thus a collection (set) of equivalence classes (sets); such a collection of classes is called a *quotient set*.

Various types of ordering relations were also discussed; any relation that is transitive is an ordering relation.

A relation that is reflexive and transitive is called a *quasi-ordering relation*.

If $R$ is a relation on $S$ and if, for every $x, y \in S$, we always have either $x \, R \, y$ or $y \, R \, x$ (possibly both), then $R$ is said to be *connected on* $S$.

A quasi-ordering relation that is connected is called a *weak ordering relation*.

A quasi-ordering relation whose equivalence relation is the identity is called a *partial ordering relation*.

A connected partial ordering relation is called a *simple ordering*.

A connected relation that is transitive and asymmetric is called a *strong ordering relation*, or a *linear ordering*.

A relation that is transitive and irreflexive is sometimes called a *preference relation*.

Next, a certain special class of relations, *called functions*, were discussed. First, the notion of a *mapping* was introduced. A *mapping* $F$ of a set $A$ *into* a set $B$, symbolized $F: A \rightarrow B$, is a *rule of correspondence* that assigns to each $a \in A$ some element $b \in B$. The correspondent, $b$, is called the *image* of $a$. If more than one element in $A$ is assigned a unique correspondent $b \in B$, the mapping is said to be *many-one*; if a single $a \in A$ has more than one image in $B$, the mapping is said to be *one-many*; finally, if every $a \in A$ has a unique correspondent $b \in B$, the mapping is said to be *one-to-one*, or *one-one*.

Often $b = F(a)$, or $b = Fa$, is written to indicate the association between elements $a \in A$ and $b \in B$. That is to say, $F(a)$ is used to symbolize the image of $a$. As long as the mapping is *not* one-many, it is customary to speak of $b$ as a *function* of $a$, particularly when the mapping is from a set of numbers to a set of numbers. The notation $b = F(a)$ is then read "$b$ is a function of $a$."

Stated another way: If $F$ is a binary relation from $A$ to $B$, we say that $F$ is a *functional relation*, or *function, from A to B*, just in case whenever $(a, b) \in F$ (that is, $b = F(a)$) and $(a, c) \in F$ (that is, $c = F(a)$), then $b = c$.

If we are given a set $\mathfrak{D}$ and a rule $F$ that assigns some image-element to every element of $\mathfrak{D}$, then $F$ is called a *function on* $\mathfrak{D}$ and $\mathfrak{D}$ is spoken of as the *domain* of the function. If $x \in \mathfrak{D}$, we denote the object $y$ assigned to $x$ (under the mapping $F$) by $F(x)$ and call it the *value* of $F$ at $x$. The set $\mathfrak{R}$ of all images $F(x)$ of $x$ called the *range* of $F$. Thus, $x \in \mathfrak{D}$ maps under $F$ on $y \in \mathfrak{R}$ and we write $y = F(x)$.

If every $b \in B$ is the image of some $a \in A$, the mapping is said to be *onto*; if there is at least one $b \in B$ that is not the image of some $a \in A$, the mapping is said to be *into*. If this matter is to be left open, the mapping is said to be a mapping of $A$ *on* $B$ or a mapping from $A$ *to* $B$.

If $F: A \to B$ is a mapping, then the mapping $F^{-1}: B \to A$ is called the *inverse* mapping. If $x \in A$ and $F(x) \in B$ (that is, $F(x)$ is the image of $x$), then $F^{-1}(x) \in A$ is called the *inverse image* of $F(x) \in B$. Alternatively, if $y = F(x)$—which says that $y$ is the image of $x$—then $x = F^{-1}(y)$ is called the *inverse* image of $x$. It is important to bear in mind that if the mapping $F: A \to B$ is a function, then the mapping $F^{-1}: B \to A$ need not be a function. However, whenever a function $F: A \to B$ is a one-one mapping onto, the inverse mapping $F^{-1}: B \to A$ will also be a function called the *inverse function*.

Finally, the notion of an *operation* on a set, in particular a *binary operation*, was introduced. A binary operation on a set $S$ is a function from $S \times S$ to $S$. In other words, it is a mapping from certain ordered couples in $S \times S$ to elements in $S$. A typical example is ordinary addition on the set of real numbers, which assigns to each real number pair $(a, b)$ a unique real number called the sum of $a$ and $b$. Since the sum of every pair of real numbers is always a real number, the set of real numbers is said to be closed under addition. More formally: If $F: A \times A \to A$ is an operation and $B \subseteq A$, then $B$ is said to be *closed under the operation* of $F$ whenever $F(B \times B) \subseteq B$.

## EXERCISES

1. Let $A = \{1, 2, 3\}$, $B = \{a, b\}$, and $C = \{u, v\}$. What is $A \times (B \times C)$? (Hint: This is a collection of ordered pairs whose second elements are themselves ordered pairs.)

2. Prove:
   (a) $A \times (B \cup C) = (A \times B) \cup (A \times C)$.
   (b) $A \times (B \cap C) = (A \times B) \cap (A \times C)$.

3. Let $S = \{1, 2, 3, 4, 5, 6\}$; graph the relation "is-a-multiple-of" on $S$ (use solid dots to exhibit the relation as in Figure 3). What is the domain of the relation? The range?

4. Let $S = \{1, 2, 3, 4, 5, 6\}$; graph the relation: "differ-by-exactly-two"— that is, if $x \in S$ (if $x$ is any one of the numbers in $S$) and $y \in S$, then $x - y = 2$ or $y - x = 2$. Give the domain and range of this relation.

5. Let $S = \{1, 2, 3, 4, 5, 6\}$; graph $R = \{(x, y) \mid y = 2\}$ and give the domain and range. Do the same for $R = \{(x, y) \mid x = 3\}$.

6. Let $S = \{1, 2, 3\}$ and $R = \{(1, 2), (2, 2), (2, 3), (1, 1), (3, 2), (3, 3)\}$.
   (a) Is $R$ a transitive relation?
   (b) Is it reflexive?
   (c) Symmetric?

7. May a relation be reflexive without being either transitive or symmetric?

8. May a relation be reflexive and transitive but not symmetric? Think of some examples.

9. May a relation be transitive without being reflexive and symmetric?

10. May a relation be symmetric without being reflexive and transitive?

11. Is it possible to have relations that are neither transitive nor symmetric nor reflexive?

12. Is it possible for a relation to be reflexive and symmetric and yet not be transitive?

13. Prove that if $(a, b) \in R$ and $R$ is symmetric and transitive, then $R$ must be reflexive. Does this prove that reflexivity is not independent of transitivity and symmetry?

14. Consider the remainders when the set of positive integers are divided by 3. Thus, 3 divides into 8 twice and leaves a remainder of 2. Similarly, 3 divides into 5 once and leaves a remainder of 2. Thus, we may say that 5 and 8 are "equivalent" in this regard: they both leave the same remainder when divided by 3 and so we will put them in one equivalence class (set): $\{5, 8, \ldots\}$.
   (a) Give another half-dozen or so elements in this class. Notice that 2 divided by 3 leaves a remainder of 2. (We would say, "3 goes into 2 zero times with a remainder of 2.")
   (b) Write some of the members of the class containing all positive integers that give a remainder of 0 when divided by 3. (These, of course, are the numbers that 3 divides exactly, with no remainder.)
   (c) Give some members for the remaining class or classes.
   (d) Do these classes partition the set of positive integers? What is the union of the classes? What is their intersection?

15. Imagine a long tape measure that is to be wrapped around an equilateral triangle that is one inch on each side, as shown in the accompanying sketch. At each corner of the triangle list some of the numbers from the tape that will lie on top of each other as the tape is wound. Notice that the numbers you get at the corner labeled zero are those that leave a remainder of zero

on division by 3; the numbers at the corner labeled 1 are those that leave a remainder of 1 on division by 3; and so on.

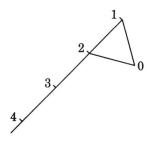

16. Do Exercise 15 for a square instead of a triangle.

17. Call the class whose *remainders* in Exercise 16 are zero, Ø; call the class whose remainder are one, I; and call the remaining two classes II and III, respectively. Notice that the sum of any two elements from, say, I and II gives an element in III. Thus, for example, $1 + 2 = 3, 5 + 2 = 7, 5 + 6 = 11$, and so on, where 1 and 5 come from the class called I, 2 comes from the class called II, and 3, 7, and 11 appear in class number III. We will write these results as

$$I + II = III,$$

$$II + II = \emptyset,$$

$$II + III = I,$$

and so on, the last result signifying that the sum of any 2 elements from, for example, classes II and III gives an element from class I. We have here the basis for an arithmetic involving exactly four symbols: Ø, I, II, III. Fill in the following addition and multiplication tables. (Notice, for example, that $I \cdot II = II$, since the product of any element in I, say 5, by an element in II, say 2, gives an element in II, namely 10.)

| + | Ø | I | II | III |
|---|---|---|----|-----|
| Ø | | | | |
| I | | | | |
| II | | | | |
| III | | | | |

| · | Ø | I | II | III |
|---|---|---|----|-----|
| Ø | | | | |
| I | | | | |
| II | | | | |
| III | | | | |

What elements function as identity elements? Does every element have an inverse under $(+)$? Under $(\cdot)$?

18. Consider the set $P \times P$ of ordered pairs of positive integers and let $R$ be a relation on $P \times P$ defined by $(a, b) R (c, d)$ if, and only if, $ad = bc$. Prove that $R$ is an equivalence relation and thus partitions $P \times P$ into equivalence classes.

19. Suppose $R$ in Exercise 18 is defined such that $(a, b)\ R\ (c, d)$ if, and only if, $a + d = b + c$. Prove that $R$ is an equivalence relation.

20. Show that if $Q$ is a quasi-ordering relation and $x\ R\ y$ is defined to be $(x\ Q\ y$ and $y\ Q\ x)$, then $R$ is an equivalence relation. (Hint: You must show that $R$, as defined, is reflexive, symmetric, and transitive.)

21. Prove that every equivalence relation is a quasi-ordering.

22. Show that if $W$ is a quasi-ordering relation and $x\ R\ y$ is defined to be $(x\ W\ y)$ and (not $y\ W\ x$), then $R$ is transitive and asymmetric. This is also an example of a *preference relation*, since an asymmetric relation is also irreflexive. (Recall that a preference relation is defined as one that is transitive and irreflexive.)

23. If $P$ is a preference relation on a set, $S$, it may happen that there is an element $x \in S$ such that there is no $y \in S$ for which $y\ P\ x$. In this case, $x$ is called a *maximal* element of $S$. If $S$ contains exactly one such $x$, it is called the *maximum*. Similarly, if there is no $y$ such that $x\ P\ y$, then $x$ is called minimal; if it is unique, it is called *the minimum*. Prove that every preference relation on a finite set $S$ has at least one maximal and one minimal element.

24. Prove that the converse of a weak ordering relation is also a weak ordering relation.

25. Prove that the converse of a preference relation is also a preference relation.

26. Let $x\ M\ y$ mean "$x$ is a multiple of $y$" on the set of positive integers.
    (a) Is $M$ a quasi-order?
    (b) Is it a weak order?
    (c) Is it a partial order?
    (d) Is it a strong order?
    (e) Is it a simple order?

27. Do Exercise 26 for the case where $D$ stands for "$x$ divides $y$ (exactly)." Notice that $y\ D\ x$ is the converse of $x\ M\ y$.

28. Let $M$ be as in Exercise 26 on the set $S = \{1, 2, 3, 4, 5, 6\}$. Does the weak order possess any maximal or minimal elements?

29. Prove that if $S$ is a finite set that can be linearly ordered, then every subset of $S$ has both a maximum and a minimum.

30. You will recall that by a function $F: A \rightarrow B$ is meant any subset of $A \times B$ among whose ordered pairs each member of $A$ appears exactly once as a first member. For example, if $A = \{a_1, a_2\}$ and $B = \{b_1, b_2, b_3\}$, then the subset of $A \times B$ whose members are $(a_1, b_1)$ and $(a_2, b_2)$ is a function on $A$ to $B$. Another example is the subset of $A \times B$ whose members are $(a_1, b_3)$ and $(a_2, b_3)$.
    (a) List the remaining seven functions $F: A \rightarrow B$.
    (b) For each $x \in A$, $f(x)$ is that element of $B$ which is assigned to $x$ by the function $F$. Thus, for example, $f(a_1) = b_1$ and $f(a_2) = b_2$. Since there are altogether nine functions, let's call the one just written $f_1$. Then another function has the property that $f_2(a_1) = b_3$ and $f_2(a_2) = b_3$. Write the remaining seven functions in this form.

**31.** The set of all single-valued functions defined for elements of the set $A$, whose *values* are elements of the set $B$, is sometimes symbolized by $B^A$. We have just found (Exercise 30) that the set $B^A$ contains nine functions. List the functions in the set $A^B$. This set will have eight functions. In general, if $A$ has $m$ elements and $B$ has $n$, $A^B$ will be composed of $m^n$ different functions.

**32.** Let $S$ be the set of all real numbers.
(a) Consider $f(x) = x^3$, where $x \in S$. What is the domain, $\mathfrak{D}$, of $f$? What is the range, $\mathfrak{R}$? Is the inverse $f^{-1}$ of $f$ also a function? What is the image of 2 under $f$—that is, find $f(2)$. Find $f(4), f(-4), f(1), f(-1), f(0), f(-2)$, $f^{-1}(8), f^{-1}(-8), f^{-1}(-4), f^{-1}(16)$.
(b) Answer the above questions for the function $f(x) = x^4$.

**33.** Plot the following sets on the real line (the line whose points correspond to real numbers).
(a) $\{x \mid x > -5\}$.
(b) $\{x \mid x < 2\}$.
(c) $\{x \mid x < 0\}$.
(d) $\{x \mid x > 0\}$.
(e) $\{x \mid x \geq 0\}$.
(f) $\{x \mid x > 0\} \cup \{x \mid x < 0\}$.
(g) $\{x \mid x > 0\} \cap \{x \mid x < 0\}$.
(h) $\{x \mid x \geq 0\} \cap \{x \mid x \leq 0\}$.
(i) $\{x \mid x \leq 2\} \cup \{x \mid x \geq 5\}$.

**34.** Plot the following sets in the plane.
(a) $2x + 3y = 12$.
(b) $2x + 3y < 12$.
(c) $2x + 3y > 12$.

**35.** Plot $f(x) = x^3$ and $f(x) = x^4$. Do these plots have the same general shape as $f(x) = x^5$ and $f(x) = x^6$? Can this be generalized to the cases $f(x) = x^n$, where, on the one hand, $n$ is odd and, on the other, $n$ is even?

**36.** If $e$ is an identity element, show that it is unique. (Hint: Start out by supposing that there is another identity element $e'$ and show that then $e' = e$—thus showing there can be only one since any "other" is equal to $e$.)

**37.** Show that where there is an identity element and when the operation $*$ is associative—that is, $a * (b * c) = (a * b) * c$—then the inverse of an element is unique. (Hint: Show that if $i$ and $i'$ are inverses of the same element $a$, then $i' = i$.)

**38.** Let $\varphi: N \times N \to N$ be the operation of multiplication, where $N$ is the set of natural numbers and 1 is the identity. What is the inverse of 1? Of 2?

**39.** State whether the following sets are closed under the operations mentioned
(a) The set of integers under division.
(b) The set of natural numbers under subtraction.
(c) The set of rational numbers under subtraction.
(d) The set of rational numbers under division.

40. Consider ordinary multiplication on the set $S = \{1, -1, I, -I\}$, where $I = \sqrt{-1}$ so that $I^2 = -1$ (that is, $I$ is a number whose square is $-1$, a so-called "imaginary" number, since there is no "real" number whose square is negative). Answer the following questions.

(a) Is the system closed under ordinary multiplication (that is, does the product of any 2 elements in $S$ always result in an element in $S$)?

(b) Does every element in $S$ possess an inverse?

(c) Is there an identity element in $S$?

# 5/ Graph Theory

## 5.1 Ordinary, Directed, and Oriented Graphs

To anyone who has ever picked up a book on Topology for the first (and probably the last) time it may seem bizarre indeed—if not downright unintelligible—for the present writer to claim that an amoeba, a public utility, and the G.O.P. are all examples of Topological Spaces. How can this be? What is a Topological Space anyway? *Prima facie*, the answer is simplicity itself, but its elaboration within the setting of general Topology would take us into rather murky waters. Instead, we shall deal only with a small corner of topology pertaining to *Graph Theory* and, in particular, pretty much confine ourselves to the Theory of *Directed Graphs*—or *Digraphs* for short. But a few more words of a general nature may be enlightening.

In elementary mathematics we're told that a "line" is a "collection" of "points" (Euclid, for example, defined it as such). A line, however, is no more a collection of points than a brain is simply a collection of neurons, a house is a collection of bricks, or a mob of people at a subway terminal is an organization. What distinguishes a line (as a geometrical—topological—object) from just any loose aggregate of points is the *structure* imposed on the points, the *relationships* among neighboring points. Just so with a Topological Space: it consists of certain sets of points bearing certain relationships to each other. A bit more precisely: A collection of points that are in no way related to one another (except that they happen to have been gathered into a "collection") is merely a *set*, but not a *space*. If, however, certain *relations* are postulated among the points (that is, if the set is *structured*), then the set is called a space. If, in particular, certain special conditions are fulfilled by the collection of subsets of the set, the space is called a *topological space*.

So too with sets of people forming an organization (or neurons forming a nervous system, and the like). An organization (whether it be a rail system for the transportation of goods, a communications network for the distribution of messages, a corporation, or a political party), in general is a *structured* collection of "points" (people, neurons, telephones, and so on) related in certain ways. Organizational integrity and homogeneity are maintained through the imposition of certain *relations* among the "elements" comprising the organization. These relations are the glue that holds the organizational framework together. For example, the relation "gives assignments to" (*x* gives assignments to *y*) imposes a *command structure* on the organization; the relation "can talk to" binds the people (and ancillary equipment) together in a *communications structure*; and so on.

The differences and similarities among organizations (organisms or corporations) are not to be sought *only* on the basis of a comparison between certain special elements (organs or departments) comprising them, no matter how similar or dissimilar these may appear. The interplay among the various components comprising an organization (the "chain of command," the information- and energy-flow patterns) are crucial to its characterization. Two organizations may appear almost identical when compared component for component (as do a man and an ape when compared organ for organ) yet be poles apart qualitatively. By the same token, two organizations may, appear different in form and yet be essentially *homeomorphic* (that is, alike in form or topologically equivalent, like a teacup and a doughnut). Again, certain basic relations among the "departments" comprising an "organization" (or the organs comprising different organisms, or the parts of speech comprising the grammars of different languages, or the complexes forming different neuroses) are the same no matter what the organization.

For example, the amount of information flowing into a department depends upon its location in the organizational hierarchy. At the very top we may have only one man (such as the President of a Company, the Chairman of the Board of a Corporation, or the Commander-in-Chief of the Air Force). But no matter how these topmost echelons are characterized, as information flows upward and into them it becomes aggregated and condensed; as it flows down it becomes diffused and ramified. This aspect of the situation will be found not to vary from one organization to another. Stated mathematically, this last remark says that certain organizations can be *mapped* on others in such a way as to preserve certain basic relations under the mapping. A rather prosaic example that springs to mind is the relation of rank in the military. Evidently, the Army can be mapped on the Air Force in such a way that the relation of rank is preserved. Thus, these organizations are homeomorphic (when, topologically speaking, the "neighborhood" or "closed set" of a man consists, say, of all men of lower rank).

Readers who have been exposed to some advanced calculus or who have dipped into a book on topology will recall the big fuss over the notion of the collection of points in the "neighborhood" (usually called open or closed sets in topology) of a given point and how such neighborhoods are mapped under various transformations. Part of the intricacy of the subject lies with our dealing there with infinite collections—indeed, nondenumerably infinite collections—of points. Since all of the collections we will be considering here (men, departments in an organization, nodes in a communications network, and so on) will be finite, there's no need for us to invoke the full machinery of topology. Furthermore, as you may have gathered from the previous paragraphs, the "neighborhoods" of our "space" will consist only of simple binary relations (such as: $x$ communicates with $y$) among the finite collections of "points." This leads us straight to the single definition that is the starting point for the theory of digraphs. It may be regarded as the definition of a certain kind of (non-Euclidean) space. (In the last chapter we will study yet another kind of space, a so-called probability space.)

A *digraph* $D$ is a collection $(V, R)$ such that $V$ is a finite, nonempty set of elements, $V = (n_1, n_2, \ldots, n_m)$, and $R$ is a binary relation on $V$ such that if $n_i R n_j$, then $n_i \neq n_j$.

The elements of $V$ will be called *nodes;* the elements of $R$ will be called *disegs* (directed segments). Notice that $R$ is a set of ordered couples and that whereas every element in $R$ is an element in $V$, the converse is not necessarily true.

Pictorially, a digraph may be represented as shown in Figure 18. The nodes of the digraphs are represented by points (vertices) and the disegs by

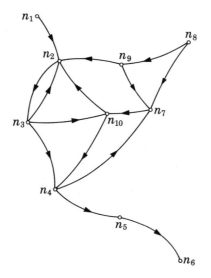

*Figure 18.* A digraph.

line segments with arrows connecting pairs of related points. The little sketch might, for example, represent a communications network with the disegs showing the flow of messages through the network. Thus, once the nodes have all been arbitrarily though distinctly labeled, $n_3 \, R \, n_4$, say, would mean that (the person at) $n_3$ sends a message to (the person at) $n_4$. Alternatively, the digraph might represent a portion of the nervous system of some simple organism with synapses shown by nodes and with afferent and efferent neurons shown by disegs. Again, the sketch might represent the flow of current through an electrical circuit, or of fluid through a system of pipelines, or of traffic through a network of one-way streets (note the single two-way street); it might even represent kinship relations among a group of people, and so on and on.

Some of the questions we might want to ask and for which the theory of digraphs supplies answers are: What is the shortest path through the network (that is, starting at $n_i$, how can $n_j$ be reached traversing the shortest number of disegs)? What is the "center" of the graph (that is, is there a node that is "central" in some sense to be defined)? If the disegs represent a set of interrelated functions (for example, activities to be performed in the execution of a task, or interrelated biochemical reactions in the production of a protein, or interrelated physiological functions in the response to a stimulus), which node is the most "critical" (in the sense that it has the largest number of direct *and indirect* dependent functions)? Again, is there a node (or set of nodes) that might become isolated from the rest by the failure of a very small number of disegs, so that we may strengthen these weak spots by adding more disegs? I shall return to some of these questions (and others) shortly. But first, a few comments on the definition above are important.

What makes digraph theory so exciting is its wide range of applicability and the extraordinary fact that such a rich stream of mathematics can flow from such a humble source. After all (assuming we know what we mean by a finite, nonempty collection of elements), the starting point of digraph theory is a single term, $R$ ("Relation") and a single postulate:* $R$ is irreflexive (by which we mean that if $n_i \, R \, n_j$, then $n_i \neq n_j$). But herein lies graph theory's great generality. By leaving as much as possible unsaid at the beginning, we open the door to many different interpretations of "digraph" running the gamut from amoeba to society. The five postulates of ordinary geometry, on the other hand, do not admit of many other interpretations outside of the customary one in terms of lines and points drawn on a sheet of paper.

Now, if we add just one additional restriction to the definition above, to the effect that $R$ is *asymmetric* (if we have $n_i \, R \, n_j$ then we *cannot* also have $n_j \, R \, n_i$), the graphs are called *oriented graphs*. Evidently, this will somewhat

---

* It will be recalled that a Field (for example, ordinary algebra) is based on eleven postulates; even ordinary plane geometry is based on five (according to Euclid, anyway).

narrow the range of problems to which we can apply the theory. Geometrically, it is tantamount to not permitting more than one diseg between any node pair so that, for example, traffic-flow problems would be confined to situations dealing with systems of one-way streets only. Finally, if all the arrows are removed from the sketch, leaving the lines and vertices exactly as they are, the resulting figure is representative of an *ordinary* (or *linear*) *graph*. Although it is appropriate to continue speaking of disegs in the case of oriented graphs (since an oriented graph is simply a digraph without two-way disegs), this term is evidently inapposite in the case of ordinary graphs; here one speaks, simply, of *segments* or *segs* of the (ordinary) graph.* To summarize: $R$ in the case of an ordinary graph is symmetric; in the case of an oriented graph it is asymmetric, and in the case of a digraph, meso-symmetric. In the first case we do not even bother to orient the segments.

Let us return to an examination of the digraph in Figure 18 to see what properties we can discover and to develop some useful terminology.

## 5.2   Some Terminology Pertaining to Graphs

In order to help fix ideas and to introduce certain terminology pertaining to oriented graphs, let us consider a specific example. Suppose the graph of Figure 18 represents a communications network. In this context, certain names quite naturally suggest themselves for some of the nodes. Thus a node like $n_1$, which only transmits messages, may be called a *transmitter*. Depending on the context, this node may also be called, variously, an *origin*, a *source*, or an *input*. We will settle on the term *source* since it is rather noncommittal. Again, a node like $n_6$ might be called a *receiver* or, alternatively, a *terminus*, *sink*, or *output*. We settle on *sink*. A node like $n_5$ serves only to relay messages; it might be called a *"through-put."* We will settle on the term *carrier* for this kind of node. The remaining nodes will be called *ordinary* nodes.

We will want to define these special nodes in some simple way. This can be done as follows. We first define the *in-degree*, *out-degree*, and total *degree* of a node.

The *in-degree* of a node $n_j$, $d_i(n_j)$, is a nonnegative integer giving the number of disegs radiating *toward* (or converging on) $n_j$. The *out-degree* of a node $n_j$, $d_o(n_j)$, is a nonnegative integer giving the number of disegs radiating *away from* (diverging from) $n_j$. The *degree* of $d(n_j)$ of a node $n_j$ is defined as $d(n_j) = d_i(n_j) + d_o(n_j)$.

Thus, we can now define a source as a node for which $d_i = 0$ and $d_o \geqslant 1$, a sink as a node for which $d_o = 0$ and $d_i \geq 1$, and a carrier as a node for which $d_i = d_o = 1$. The values of $d_i$ and $d_o$ can be found very quickly by

---

* Some authors, in this context, use the term *edge* and refer to *disegs* as *arcs*.

glancing at the adjacency matrix (Section 5.3) of a digraph. If you think about it a moment, you will see that the sum of the in-degrees of all the nodes of a graph is equal to the sum of the out-degrees; their common value is equal to the total number of disegs in the digraph. When we come to the matrix representation of a digraph, you will see that this result is almost trivial.

As pointed out right after the definition in the previous section, while every element belonging to some ordered couple in $R$ belongs to $V$, there may be some elements in $V$ that are not part of any ordered couple in $R$. Such a node may be called an *isolate*. The reason for keeping this question open is that we want to continue using the term "digraph" when there are such isolates. Thus, in the context of our communications example, if the communications link between $n_5$ and $n_6$ is severed the resulting figure still deserves to be called a digraph, though a "disconnected" one if you will, and $n_6$ simply becomes an isolate of the digraph. The digraph in Figure 18 contains no isolates; it is an example of a *connected* digraph. But how are we to define this notion?

Evidently, the orientations of the disegs have nothing to do with the notion of connectedness. The outstanding feature of a connected digraph (or oriented graph or ordinary graph) is that every node can be reached from any other by traveling along the disegs. As we move along the disegs we will sometimes be traveling in the direction of the arrows and sometimes in the direction opposite. However, we want to ignore such orientations and are only interested in whether we will encounter all the links along the chains we are traveling. Therefore, let us define the notion of a chain.

A *chain* between $n_1$ and $n_k$ is a collection of distinct nodes $\{n_1, n_2, \ldots, n_k\}$ together with $k - 1$ *segments* $\{n_1, n_2\}, \{n_2, n_3\}, \ldots, \{n_{k-1}, n_k\}$, where $\{n_i, n_j\}$ is a segment whenever $n_i R n_j$ or $n_j R n_i$.

We can now define the notion of connectedness. A digraph (as well as an oriented and an ordinary graph) is *connected* if, and only if, for *every* pair of distinct nodes there is a chain going from one to the other.

The reason we introduced the term *chain* above is that the term *path* is reserved for a stricter notion. A (directed) *path*, $p(n_1 n_k)$, *from* $n_1$ *to* $n_k$ (notice that we do *not* speak of a path "between" two nodes) is a collection of distinct nodes $\{n_1, n_2, \ldots, n_k\}$ together with the disegs $n_1 n_2, n_2 n_3, \ldots, n_{k-1} n_k$.

We will say that a digraph is *strongly connected* whenever there is a path joining any pair of arbitrary distinct vertices. If the digraph representing a phenomenon is strongly connected, the constituent parts of that phenomenon are evidently intimately related.

We will say that any point is *reachable from* any other point in a strongly connected digraph. Every strongly connected digraph is, of course, connected in the previous sense, though the converse is obviously not true. Figure 19 illustrates the difference between the two concepts. Notice that the fact

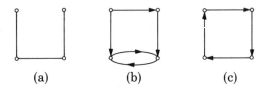

**Figure 19.** Connected graphs. (a) Connected graph.
(b) Connected digraph. (c) Strongly connected digraph.

that any node in Figure 19(c) can be reached from any other does not imply that every node is connected to every other. Digraphs (as well as oriented and ordinary graphs) for which this is true are said to be *complete*. The digraph in Figure 19(c) would be complete if the two diagonal disegs were added.

There are a good many additional notions we could introduce in this section. Instead of doing this, however, we will let you discover some of them for yourselves in the exercises, to which you might wish to turn now, before continuing with the next section. But first, let us summarize what has happened so far.

As mentioned at the beginning of this chapter, graph theory is within the province of a branch of mathematics called topology. The topologist is interested in graphs as mathematical entities and studies their properties for their own sake and, no doubt, for the intellectual enjoyment such studies afford. We hope that when you do the exercises you will share in some of this. However, it could not help but be noticed that the little sketches one sometimes used when working in graph theory bore a strong resemblance to such things as communications networks, organization charts, sociograms, and even neural networks. Thus, in recent times, workers in these areas, and indeed anyone interested in the ways the parts of something are related to each other, have been adding to the theory. We have tried to impart a feeling for how this work might proceed along purely "geometric" lines, and the exercises will give you additional insights. In the next section we take a somewhat different, and possibly simpler, tack. Whereas what has gone before might be called the "geometry" of graphs, we now propose to do a little "algebra" on graphs. This approach will allow us to study graphs using certain almost mechanical manipulations, and it places considerably less strain on the intuition than does the approach above.

## 5.3 Matrices and Digraphs

Matrix algebra provides a powerful tool for the study of digraphs (and oriented graphs too). Not only that, but it is a very powerful tool in its own right and has found extensive applications in areas running the gamut from sociology to nuclear physics. It is, therefore, appropriate that we should devote some space to the discussion of matrices. Then we shall discuss their use in the study of digraphs.

### 5.3.1 Matrices

For our purposes, it will be sufficient to describe a matrix as simply a tabular arrangement of numbers and go immediately to an illustration. Suppose two different models, Model A and Model B, of a small computer consist of three distinct components $c_1$, $c_2$, and $c_3$, each component being made up of a certain number of parts, such as transistors, resistors, and capacitors. Table 5.1 lists the numbers of parts comprising each component and Table 5.2 exhibits the numbers of components in each model.

|                    | $c_1$ | $c_2$ | $c_3$ |
| ------------------ | ----- | ----- | ----- |
| No. of transistors | 10    | 12    | 20    |
| No. of resistors   | 17    | 15    | 19    |
| No. of capacitors  | 18    | 11    | 16    |

**Table 5.1.** Parts per component matrix

|       | Model A | Model B |
| ----- | ------- | ------- |
| $c_1$ | 3       | 8       |
| $c_2$ | 2       | 4       |
| $c_3$ | 5       | 1       |

**Table 5.2.** Components per model matrix

In order to find, say, the number of parts per model, we multiply the numbers in the first *row* of the parts per component matrix by the numbers appearing in the first *column* of the components per model matrix and sum these products, as follows:

$$10 \times 3 + 12 \times 2 + 20 \times 5 = 154 \quad \text{transistors in Model A.}$$

Similarly,

$$17 \times 3 + 15 \times 2 + 19 \times 5 = 176 \quad \text{resistors in Model A}$$

and

$$18 \times 3 + 11 \times 2 + 16 \times 5 = 156 \quad \text{capacitors in Model A.}$$

Proceeding similarly with Model B, we have

$$10 \times 8 + 12 \times 4 + 20 \times 1 = 148 \quad \text{transistors in Model B,}$$

$$17 \times 8 + 15 \times 4 + 19 \times 1 = 215 \quad \text{resistors in Model B,}$$

$$18 \times 8 + 11 \times 4 + 16 \times 1 = 204 \quad \text{capacitors in Model B.}$$

These results may be displayed in the form of a parts per model matrix (Table 5.3):

|  | Model A | Model B |
|---|---|---|
| No. of transistors | 154 | 148 |
| No. of resistors | 176 | 215 |
| No. of capacitors | 156 | 204 |

*Table 5.3.* Parts per model matrix

Matrices are customarily written by placing a pair of large brackets around the tabular array of numbers. The entries in the "table" are referred to as the *elements of the matrix*. The procedure we have gone through above is symbolized in a single step as follows:

$$\begin{bmatrix} 10 & 12 & 20 \\ 17 & 15 & 19 \\ 18 & 11 & 16 \end{bmatrix} \times \begin{bmatrix} 3 & 8 \\ 2 & 4 \\ 5 & 1 \end{bmatrix} = \begin{bmatrix} 154 & 148 \\ 176 & 215 \\ 156 & 204 \end{bmatrix}.$$

Notice that the value of the element appearing in the first row and first column (upper left corner) of the resultant matrix consists of the sum of the products of the elements of the first *row* of the first matrix by the elements of the first *column* of the second matrix. The value of the element appearing in the first column and second row (176) consists of the sum of the products of the elements of the *second* row of the first matrix by the elements of the first column of the second matrix, and so on.

This example is just one justification for the rule of multiplication of matrices, which may seem bizarre the first time you are exposed to it. Another example of how the rule works is shown below.

$$\begin{bmatrix} 2 & 3 \\ 1 & 5 \\ 6 & 4 \end{bmatrix} \times \begin{bmatrix} 0 & 7 & 9 \\ 8 & 2 & 7 \end{bmatrix} = \begin{bmatrix} 2 \cdot 0 + 3 \cdot 8 & 2 \cdot 7 + 3 \cdot 2 & 2 \cdot 9 + 3 \cdot 7 \\ 1 \cdot 0 + 5 \cdot 8 & 1 \cdot 7 + 5 \cdot 2 & 1 \cdot 9 + 5 \cdot 7 \\ 6 \cdot 0 + 4 \cdot 8 & 6 \cdot 7 + 4 \cdot 2 & 6 \cdot 9 + 4 \cdot 7 \end{bmatrix}$$

$$= \begin{bmatrix} 24 & 20 & 39 \\ 40 & 17 & 44 \\ 32 & 50 & 82 \end{bmatrix}.$$

This procedure may be illustrated symbolically as follows:

$$\begin{bmatrix} a_1 & a_2 \\ b_1 & b_2 \\ c_1 & c_2 \end{bmatrix} \times \begin{bmatrix} d_1 & d_2 & d_3 \\ e_1 & e_2 & e_3 \end{bmatrix} = \begin{bmatrix} a_1d_1 + a_2e_1 & a_1d_2 + a_2e_2 & a_1d_3 + a_2e_3 \\ b_1d_1 + b_2e_1 & b_1d_2 + b_2e_2 & b_1d_3 + b_2e_3 \\ c_1d_1 + c_2e_1 & c_1d_2 + c_2e_2 & c_1d_3 + c_2e_3 \end{bmatrix}.$$

Study the pattern formed in the resultant matrix. Notice that $d_1$ and $e_1$ always occur in the sums of the products appearing in the first column, that $d_2$ and $e_2$ appear in the entries of the second column, and $d_3$ and $e_3$ appear in the entries in the last column. On the other hand, only $a$'s ($a_1$ and $a_2$) appear across the first row, only $b$'s across the second, and only $c$'s across the last row of the product matrix.

Instead of this use of different letters to represent the elements in the different rows of the matrix, there is a much neater scheme for exhibiting these elements, as shown below:

$$\begin{bmatrix} a_{11} & a_{12} & a_{13} & a_{14} \\ a_{21} & a_{22} & a_{23} & a_{24} \\ a_{31} & a_{32} & a_{33} & a_{34} \end{bmatrix}$$

The element appearing in the $i$th *row* and $j$th *column* of the matrix is symbolized by $a_{ij}$. Thus, for example, the element appearing in the third row, second column is symbolized $a_{32}$, while the element appearing in the second row and third column is symbolized $a_{23}$. Notice that the first subscript always gives the row in which the element appears (see the matrix above) while the second subscript always gives the column in which the element appears.

The matrix above is an example of what is called a $3 \times 4$ ("three-by-four") matrix. In general, a matrix with $m$ *rows* and $n$ *columns* is called an $m \times n$ ("$m$-by-$n$") matrix and the matrix is said to be of order $m \times n$.

If the matrix happens to be square and contains $n$ rows and $n$ columns, one speaks of an *nth-order* matrix or of a matrix of *order n*. In the case of a *square* matrix the elements appearing along the diagonal from $a_{11}$ (the upper left corner) to $a_{nn}$ (the lower right corner) are said to belong to the *main diagonal* of the matrix. These elements sometimes play a special role in matrix algebra.

Notice that because of the special way in which matrices are multiplied the number of *columns* in the matrix to the left of the multiplication sign must be the same as the number of *rows* in the matrix appearing to the right of the multiplication sign. When this is the case, the matrices are said to be *conformable*. Nonconformable matrices cannot be multiplied together. Notice, furthermore, that if a $p \times n$ matrix is multiplied on the left by an $m \times p$ matrix, the result is an $m \times n$ matrix. Obviously, the order in which the two matrices are multiplied is important. If $A$ and $B$ are two matrices, in general,

$$A \cdot B \neq B \cdot A.$$

Thus, matrix multiplication, in general, is noncommutative, just like the set product. In order to distinguish the two situations we say that $B$ is *premultiplied* by $A$ when $A$ appears to the left of $B$ and that $B$ is *post-multiplied* by $A$ if $A$ appears to the right of $B$.

It is time now to formalize the rule of multiplication for a pair of matrices. Symbolically, we write

$$A \times B = C$$

or, to consider a specific example,

$$\begin{bmatrix} a_{11} & a_{12} & a_{13} \\ a_{21} & a_{22} & a_{23} \end{bmatrix} \times \begin{bmatrix} b_{11} & b_{12} \\ b_{21} & b_{22} \\ b_{31} & b_{32} \end{bmatrix} = \begin{bmatrix} c_{11} & c_{12} \\ c_{21} & c_{22} \end{bmatrix}.$$

Notice that the $c_{ij}$, besides giving the location of the elements in $C$, also indicates the row and column of the two matrices that are multiplied together to get $c_{ij}$. Thus, for example, $c_{12}$ comes from combining the first *row* of $A$ with the second *column* of $B$:

$$c_{12} = a_{11}b_{12} + a_{12}b_{22} + a_{13}b_{32}.$$

Similarly,

$$c_{21} = a_{21}b_{11} + a_{22}b_{21} + a_{23}b_{31}.$$

This result, in general, will be symbolized

$$c_{ij} = a_{ik}b_{kj},$$

where the double appearance of the subscript $k$ signifies that a summation is to be performed with respect to it, the number of terms in the sum being equal to the number of rows in $A$ (which must be the same as the number of columns in $B$, of course). Thus, for example, if we multiply a matrix with 5 columns by one with 5 rows, the element $c_{ij}$ appearing at the $i$th-row and $j$th-row column of the product matrix will consist of the following sum:

$$c_{ij} = a_{i1}b_{1j} + a_{i2}b_{2j} + a_{i3}b_{3j} + a_{i4}b_{4j} + a_{i5}b_{5j}.$$

For example,

$$c_{23} = a_{21}b_{13} + a_{22}b_{23} + a_{23}b_{33} + a_{24}b_{43} + a_{25}b_{53}.$$

It is necessary to define only two more notions to prepare you for the use you will make of matrices in the next section. One is the notion of the addition

of two matrices; the rule is simple: to add a pair of matrices we simply add
the elements appearing at corresponding locations. Thus, for example,

$$\begin{bmatrix} 1 & 2 \\ 3 & 4 \end{bmatrix} + \begin{bmatrix} 5 & 6 \\ 7 & 8 \end{bmatrix} = \begin{bmatrix} 6 & 8 \\ 10 & 12 \end{bmatrix}.$$

Evidently, both matrices have to be of the same order (conformable with
respect to addition) if we are to add them.

The second notion concerns *equality* of matrices. Two matrices are
equal if, and only if, each element in one is equal to the corresponding element
in the other matrix; that is, if $A = B$ then $a_{ij} = b_{ij}$ and vice versa. Evidently,
the matrices must have exactly the same number of rows and columns.

Besides being applicable to a wide range of practical problems, matrix
algebra is a fascinating subject in its own right, as you may discover by
doing some of the exercises. It is similar to ordinary algebra in some respects
but quite different in others. For example, a square matrix containing 1's
along the main diagonal and 0's everywhere else functions as a "unity
element" under matrix multiplication (much like the number 1 in ordinary
arithmetic). Such a unity matrix is symbolized $I$ (for "identity") and has
the unique property that $A \times I = I \times A = A$.

You may recall from algebra that when the product of two real numbers
is unity, the two numbers are said to be *multiplicative inverses* of each other
(for example, $3 \times \frac{1}{3} = 1$, $\frac{5}{4} \times \frac{4}{5} = 1$, and so on). You may also recall from
algebra that every real number, except zero, possesses an inverse. This fact
is useful in solving equations. For example, if it is given that

$$5x = 2,$$

the equation may be solved for $x$ by multiplying both sides by the inverse of
5, namely, $\frac{1}{5}$, getting

$$x = \tfrac{2}{5}$$

It turns out that under certain circumstances a square matrix $A$ will possess
an inverse, symbolized $A^{-1}$, a fact which is useful for solving matrix equations. Not every square matrix possesses an inverse and, when it does,
finding the inverse is not always a simple matter (especially when the matrix
is large). Since the primary use we will be making of matrices is in the study
of digraphs, we need not invoke the full machinery of matrix algebra here.
However, Exercises 14 through 22 will give you some feeling for this subject.

### 5.3.2  The Adjacency Matrix of a Digraph

In order to write the adjacency matrix of a digraph (or an oriented
graph) proceed as follows.

Each of the $N$ nodes of a digraph is assigned a number from 1 to $N$ (in any arbitrary way) and a matrix called the *adjacency* (or *associated*) *matrix* is filled in as follows: Whenever there is a diseg going *from* the node labeled $i$ *to* the node labeled $j$, the element $m_{ij}$ occurring at the intersection of the $i$th *row* and $j$th *column* of the matrix is assigned a value of 1; otherwise the element at that location is assigned a value of 0. (See Figure 20; the numbers bordering the matrix will be explained shortly.)

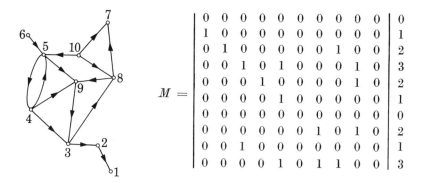

$$M =$$

| | | | | | | | | | | | |
|---|---|---|---|---|---|---|---|---|---|---|---|
| 0 | 0 | 0 | 0 | 0 | 0 | 0 | 0 | 0 | 0 | 0 |
| 1 | 0 | 0 | 0 | 0 | 0 | 0 | 0 | 0 | 0 | 1 |
| 0 | 1 | 0 | 0 | 0 | 0 | 0 | 1 | 0 | 0 | 2 |
| 0 | 0 | 1 | 0 | 1 | 0 | 0 | 0 | 1 | 0 | 3 |
| 0 | 0 | 0 | 1 | 0 | 0 | 0 | 0 | 1 | 0 | 2 |
| 0 | 0 | 0 | 0 | 1 | 0 | 0 | 0 | 0 | 0 | 1 |
| 0 | 0 | 0 | 0 | 0 | 0 | 0 | 0 | 0 | 0 | 0 |
| 0 | 0 | 0 | 0 | 0 | 0 | 1 | 0 | 1 | 0 | 2 |
| 0 | 0 | 1 | 0 | 0 | 0 | 0 | 0 | 0 | 0 | 1 |
| 0 | 0 | 0 | 0 | 1 | 0 | 1 | 1 | 0 | 0 | 3 |

*Figure 20.* A digraph and its adjacency matrix.

There are several things one notices almost at once about the digraph's adjacency matrix. Such a matrix will evidently be square and of $N$th order; furthermore, since $R$ is irreflexive, the main diagonal of the matrix will always consist entirely of zeros. If the matrix happens to be symmetrical about the main diagonal (that is, $m_{ij} = m_{ji} = 1$), then the graph is also obviously symmetrical. Of course, if the digraph is asymmetrical (as in the case of a command structure in an organization), then, whenever $m_{ij} = 1$, $m_{ji}$ will be zero. Transitivity of the digraph is somewhat more difficult to spot by simply glancing at the associated matrix. Finding out that the graph is not transitive may be simpler, since we need only find one set of disegs such that $m_{ij} = 1$ and $m_{jk} = 1$, but $m_{ik} \neq 1$ (for example, $m_{54} = 1$ and $m_{43} = 1$ in the matrix of Figure 20, but $m_{53} \neq 1$; therefore the graph is not transitive).

The sum of the elements across any particular row (shown to the right of $M$) shows at a glance the total number of nodes a particular node is connected with (for example, node 4 radiates 3 disegs to other nodes; node 7 none); the sum of the elements down a particular column shows the number of disegs a particular node receives from other nodes (for example, node 10 receives no disegs; node 9 received 3).

If we glance at these row and column sums, it is a simple matter to spot the sinks and sources in the digraph (or in an oriented graph). To find the sinks, scan the sums of the *rows* (shown to the right of the matrix $M$ in Figure 20) looking for 0's. Thus, in the present example (Figure 20), nodes 1 and 7 are sinks. To find the sources, glance across the *column* sums (shown below $M$ in Figure 20) looking for 0's. Thus, in Figure 20, nodes 6 and 10 are source nodes.

Certain additional terminology suggests itself. For example, a further distinction may be made on the basis of whether the sink receives only a single diseg, in which case it may be called an (environmental) *output node* (such as node 1, which radiates no disegs, since a 0 appears to the right of the matrix in row 1, and which is on the receiving end of a single diseg, since a 1 appears for the sum of the first *column*). Again, a further distinction may be made on the basis of whether a source node radiates but a single diseg, in which case it may be called an (environmental) *input node*. Thus, for example, the sixth-column sum is 0 while the sixth-row sum is 1, and so node 6 is an input node; the tenth-column sum is also 0, but the tenth-row sum is greater than 1 so that node 10 is a source. Incidentally, notice that the sum of either the row sums or the column sums gives the total number of disegs in the digraph:

$$(1 + 1 + 2 + 1 + 3 + 0 + 2 + 2 + 3 + 0)$$

$$= (0 + 1 + 2 + 3 + 2 + 1 + 0 + 2 + 1 + 3) = 15.$$

Certain sets of *disegs* may also be given special names: thus, the disegs connecting nodes 4 and 5 may be said to form a *loop* and the disegs connecting nodes 8, 9, and 3 may be said to form a *cycle*. Just a word about one more term because it defines an important notion, that of *homeomorphism*.

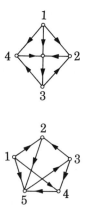

**Figure 21.** Homeomorphic digraphs.

Digraphs that are homeomorphic are structurally indistinguishable, even though they may appear quite different on the surface (Figure 21). Formally: Two digraphs $D$ and $D'$ are said to be *homeomorphic* if they each have the same number of nodes and if we can label these $n_1, n_2, \ldots, n_m$ and $n'_1, n'_2, \ldots, n'_m$, respectively, in such a way that diseg $n_i n_j$ belongs to $D$ if, and only if, $n'_i n'_j$ belongs to $D'$.

Evidently, the relation of homeomorphism is an equivalence relation for, from the definition of this relation, it should be obvious that every digraph is homeomorphic to itself; furthermore, if $D$ is homeomorphic to $D'$, then, evidently, $D'$ is homeomorphic to $D$; and, finally, if $D$ is homeomorphic to $D'$ and $D'$ to $D''$, then $D$ is homeomorphic to $D''$. Another interesting little fact (of which you should be able to convince yourself): Any two *complete, symmetric* digraphs with the same number of nodes are necessarily homeomorphic. What this means, for example, is that there is essentially only one way to set up a complete, two-way communications network on, say, 100 nodes—that is, any way of hooking up 100 telephones is as good as any other since all of the possible networks (which may *appear* different on the surface) will be structurally indistinguishable.

Let us turn now to certain matrix manipulations and show their connection with digraph theory. Suppose we have a series of interconnected tasks that must be performed in the execution of some objective (or a series of interdependent biochemical functions maintaining the integrity of some physiological process, and so on) as pictured by the accompanying digraph.

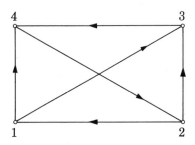

Is there some say in which we can order these tasks in terms of their "importance"? In other words, can we find certain nodes in a digraph that are more "critical" than others? Of course, we have to decide what we want to mean by "critical" and "important." One sensible way is to say that a node is more critical than another if it has more tasks dependent on it. From this standpoint, node 2 of the little system above is the most critical, for the remaining three tasks or functions (nodes) are dependent on it; if it goes, the system collapses. Next in order of importance would be node 3, for it has two tasks dependent on it; next comes node 4; and finally node 1 is last,

since no other task (node or function) depends on its existence. But consider
now the situation depicted below:

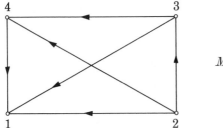

$$M = \begin{vmatrix} 0 & 0 & 1 & 1 & 2 \\ 1 & 0 & 1 & 0 & 2 \\ 0 & 0 & 0 & 1 & 1 \\ 0 & 1 & 0 & 0 & 1 \end{vmatrix}$$

How are we to order each node from most to least critical here? It turns out
that this is feasible in a sense to be defined. We must first broaden the concept
of "criticality" in the following natural way. The criticality or importance
of a task depends not only on the other tasks immediately dependent on it
but also on those tasks secondarily dependent on it (through the intermediary
of a third task). Thus, node 3 above not only has node 4 as immediate dependent, but it also has node 2 as dependent, via node 4. *Prima facie*, tasks
(nodes) 1 and 2, for example, appear equally important since they each have
two other dependent tasks. But the wary reader will have already noticed
that 1 depends on 2, so node 2 must somehow be more important. But then,
node 2 can't be too important, for it depends on the relatively weak node 4.
And what about 4? It must be fairly important, since the relatively important task 2 depends on it. And so does task 3, for that matter (via task 2).
But is it more important than 3? (Notice that it *depends* on 3—as well as on
1, of course.) Even on this simple level there is some room for argument.
You can appreciate what it would be like trying to untangle a 20-node network along these lines. The trouble is, of course, that we are trying to puzzle
the thing through *intuitively* (which is all right sometimes, for a lot of good
topology has come about in just this way). Fortunately, there exists a *formal*
approach to this question (which means that in the case of large networks
the problem is amenable to computer solution).

The result of squaring the matrix $M$ is shown below:

$$M^2 = \begin{vmatrix} 0 & 1 & 0 & 1 \\ 0 & 0 & 1 & 2 \\ 0 & 1 & 0 & 0 \\ 1 & 0 & 1 & 0 \end{vmatrix}.$$

A little thought should convince you that the entries of this matrix give the
number of 2-stage paths from every node to every other. Thus, for example,
the entries in the first row of $M^2$ show that there is one 2-stage path from
node 1 to node 2 (namely, $1 \rightarrow 4 \rightarrow 2$) and one 2-stage path from node 1 to 4

$(1 \rightarrow 3 \rightarrow 4)$; similarly, there is one 2-stage path from node 2 to 3 and two 2-stage paths from node 2 to node 4; and so on.

Now consider the sum of $M$ and $M^2$:

$$M + M^2 = \begin{array}{|cccc|c|} 0 & 1 & 1 & 2 & 4 \\ 1 & 0 & 2 & 2 & 5 \\ 0 & 1 & 0 & 1 & 2 \\ 1 & 1 & 1 & 0 & 3 \end{array}$$

The sums of the rows of this matrix now give the total number of 1- and 2-stage dependencies among the nodes. On the basis of these row sums, the nodes can now be ordered: $2 > 1 > 4 > 3$ (where $>$ means "is more important than," say). Succinctly, if $M$ is the matrix associated with a digraph, the entries across the rows of $M^n$ give the number of $n$-diseg-long paths from each node to every other. And the sum of the rows of the matrix $M + M^2 + M^3 + \cdots + M^n$ will give the total number of 1-, 2-, ..., $n$-stage paths from each node to every other. Stated another way: the entries along the rows of $M^n$ give the set of nodes reachable from each node in $n$ steps. Incidentally, notice that the value of the entries $m_{ii}$ along the main diagonal of $M^n$ give the number of *cycles* of length $n$ containing node $i$.

We have just seen a graph-theoretic interpretation for the operation of raising a matrix to a power. An even simpler operation is that of taking the *transpose* of a matrix (for example, interchanging its rows with its columns). This, too, has a facile interpretation in graph-theoretic terms. If one simply reverses the direction of all the disegs (arrows) of a digraph, its associated matrix will be the transpose of the matrix associated with the original digraph. From the standpoint of relations the transpose of a matrix associated with a digraph corresponds to the converse of a relation. (Recall that $R$ is the converse of $R'$ if, whenever $x \, R \, y$, then $y \, R' \, x$; for example, "is the husband of" is the converse of "is the wife of"; note that "is the mate of" is its own converse).

We give one more example which illustrates that not only the standard matrix operations find interpretation in digraph theory. The reader who was dismayed on first being exposed to the queer row-by-column rule for multiplying matrices will be pleased to learn of the *Hadamard product* of two matrices. This is found by simply multiplying the two matrices element by element as shown below:

$$\begin{array}{|cc|} 5 & 1 \\ 2 & 6 \\ 4 & 3 \end{array} \otimes \begin{array}{|cc|} 2 & 3 \\ 1 & 5 \\ 6 & 4 \end{array} = \begin{array}{|cc|} 10 & 3 \\ 2 & 30 \\ 24 & 12 \end{array}.$$

The Hadamard product of the matrices associated with a couple of digraphs, $D_1$ and $D_2$, will result in the associated matrix of a digraph which can be

considered as the intersection $D_1 \cap D_2$ (in the set-theoretic sense) of the
original digraphs. The digraph $D_1 \cap D_2$ will contain a diseg $n_i n_j$ if, and only
if, this diseg belongs to both $D_1$ and $D_2$ (see below):

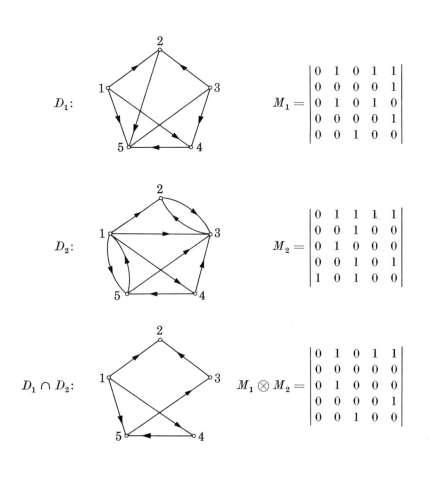

Here is a simple interpretation. Let the digraphs represent a sequence of
steps to be followed in the manufacture of some item and suppose that one
digraph represents the quickest way of doing the job while the other represents the cheapest way, then $D_1 \cap D_2$ represents the quickest and cheapest
way of manufacturing the item.

We might as well round out the discussion by introducing the second
well-known set-theoretic operation and illustrate the union, $D_1 \cup D_2$, of two
digraphs. The matrix associated with $D_1 \cup D_2$ is found by simply adding
$M_1 + M_2$ in the customary way, except that we take the Boolean sum of the

elements—which sum, you recall, is defined so that $1 + 1 = 1$ ($0 + 1 = 1 + 0 = 1$ and $0 + 0 = 0$, as usual, however). The result is shown below:

$D_1 \cup D_2$:

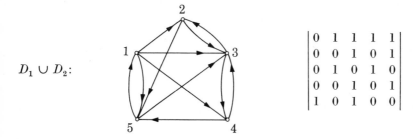

$$\begin{vmatrix} 0 & 1 & 1 & 1 & 1 \\ 0 & 0 & 1 & 0 & 1 \\ 0 & 1 & 0 & 1 & 0 \\ 0 & 0 & 1 & 0 & 1 \\ 1 & 0 & 1 & 0 & 0 \end{vmatrix}$$

This evidently represents the digraph of the manufacturing process that is either cheapest or quickest (possibly both). Incidentally, if one wanted to find the digraph of the process that is either cheaper or quicker, but *not* both (called the *symmetric difference* in set theory), then one would still form the sum of the two associated matrices, only (instead of Boolean) one would use modulo 2 arithmetic wherein $1 + 1 = 0$ (the remaining sums being the same as before).

We close this chapter with an example from ordinary graph theory to give the reader a feeling for the nature of the problems dealt with there. A number of small towns are connected by a system of direct routes. A wholesaler wants to know the minimum number of warehouses required, and in which towns these should be located, so that his retail outlets, one in each town, can be reached directly. Suppose the map of the region appears as in the accompanying sketch. (The towns have been numbered arbitrarily, for convenience.) Can you find the one or more (least number of) towns (nodes)

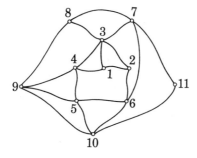

from which every other town (node) can be reached directly? Algorithms exist for solving this problem, though in this simple case their use is not required. But imagine trying to solve the problem for twenty towns connected by thirty routes.

One can go a long way along the route sketched in this chapter and then take off on a new tack by assigning "weights" to the disegs. But this would take us much too far afield. The theory of weighted graphs is a subject in its own right, but it presupposes many of the techniques of graph theory such as we have explored here. If the weights are interpreted as "flows" (such as bits/sec in a communications network, gallons/min in pipeline problems, or cars/hour along highways), we get into the areas of flow graphs. If the weights are probabilities, we get into the area of Markov processes and state (transition) diagrams. Such weighted digraphs are sometimes called *nets* or *networks*. There are a number of good standard texts in these areas which the specialist may wish to consult. (Incidentally, the answer to the problem above is towns 3 and 10.)

## 5.4   Summary

A directed graph, or *digraph*, $D$ is a collection $(V, R)$ such that $V$ is a finite nonempty set of elements (called *nodes*) and $R$ is a binary relation on $V$ such that if $n_i\ R\ n_j$ (where $n_i$ and $n_j \in V$) then $n_i \neq n_j$. The elements of $R$ are called directed segments or *disegs* (or *arcs*).

Pictorially, a digraph may be depicted as a network of interconnected points. The points represent nodes, and lines (with arrows) connecting the points represent disegs. Whenever an arrow points *from* a node $n_i$ *to* a node $n_j$ we write $n_i\ R\ n_j$.

When the relation $R$ is asymmetric, one speaks, in particular, of an *oriented* graph. When $R$ is symmetric, one speaks of a *linear graph*, or simply, a *graph*. In this case the elements of $R$ are called *segments* (or *edges*).

A node $n_i$ such that $n_i\ R\ n_j$, for at least one node $n_j$, but for which there is no $n_j$ such that $n_j\ R\ n_i$, is called a *source*. Pictorially, no diseg impinges on such a node and at least one diseg radiates away from it. Alternatively, if a node only receives disegs but radiates none (a node, $n_j$, such that $n_i\ R\ n_j$ for at least one node $n_i$, but not $n_j\ R\ n_i$), it is called a *sink*. A node that receives a single diseg and radiates a single diseg is called a *carrier*. All other nodes are called *ordinary*.

The *in-degree* of a node $n_j$, $d_i(n_j)$, is a nonnegative integer giving the number of disegs converging on $n_j$. The *out-degree* of a node $n_j$, $d_0(n_j)$, is a nonnegative integer giving the number of disegs diverging from $n_j$.

The *degree* of a node is defined as

$$d(n_j) = d_i(n_j) + d_o(n_j).$$

Whenever $n_i\ R\ n_j$ or $n_j\ R\ n_i$, we speak of the *segment* $\{n_i, n_j\}$. A *chain* between $n_1$ and $n_k$ is a collection of distinct nodes $\{n_1, n_2, \ldots, n_k\}$ together with $k - 1$ segments:

$$\{n_1, n_2\}, \{n_2, n_3\}, \ldots, \{n_{k-1}, n_k\}.$$

A digraph is said to be *connected* if, and only if, there is a chain for every pair of distinct nodes.

A (directed) *path, $p(n_1, n_k)$ from $n_1$ to $n_k$* is a collection of distinct nodes $\{n_1, n_2, \ldots, n_k\}$ together with the disegs $n_1n_2, n_2n_3, \ldots, n_{k-1}n_k$.

A digraph is *strongly connected* whenever there is a path joining any pair of arbitrary distinct vertices. Any point is said to be *reachable* from any other point in a strongly connected digraph.

A graph in which every node is connected to every other is said to be *complete*.

The matrix associated with a digraph is a tabular array of 0's and 1's. Whenever $n_i \, R \, n_j$, the matrix contains a 1 at the location of the $i$th row and $j$th column; otherwise that location contains a 0. This matrix is called the *adjacency* matrix of the digraph.

The sum of the numbers across any particular row of the adjacency matrix gives the out-degree of any particular node; the sum of the numbers down any particular column gives the in-degree of any particular node.

Row sums of sinks are zero and row sums of sources are one. If the sum of the numbers in the $i$th row of the adjacency matrix is zero while the sum of the numbers in the $i$th column is one, $n_i$ is called an *output node*; conversely, $n_i$ is called an *input node* whenever the $i$th row sum is one while the $i$th column sum is zero.

Two digraphs $D$ and $D'$ are said to be *homeomorphic* (or *topologically equivalent*) if they each have the same number of nodes and if we can label these $n_1, n_2, \ldots, n_m$ and $n_1', n_2', \ldots, n_m'$, respectively, in such a way that diseg $n_i n_j$ belongs to $D$ if, and only if, $n_i'n_j'$ belongs to $D'$.

If $A$ is the adjacency matrix associated with a particular digraph, then the entries in $A^n$ give the number of $n$-diseg-long paths from every node to every other.

If $D_1$ and $D_2$ are a pair of digraphs with associated matrices $A_1$ and $A_2$, then the matrix associated with $D_1 \cap D_2$ is found by taking the element-wise (or Hadamard) product, $A_1 \otimes A_2$, of the two matrices.

The matrix associated with $D_1 \cup D_2$ is found by simply adding $A_1 + A_2$ in the usual way, except that the sum of the elements is the Boolean sum (wherein $1 + 1 = 1$, while $1 + 0 = 0 + 1 = 1$ and $0 + 0 = 0$ in the usual way). If $(D_1 - D_2) \cup (D_2 - D_1)$—the symmetric difference of the two digraphs—is sought, one simply uses modulo 2 arithmetic instead (in which $1 + 1 = 0$) in forming sums of elements from $A_1$ and $A_2$.

# EXERCISES

1.  In the definition of a digraph it is left open whether the relation is symmetric or not and transitive or not. (The single postulate says only that $R$ is irreflexive.) Suppose you are studying a phenomenon that is governed by an irreflexive relation, and suppose that the relation also happens to be symmetric and transitive. What can you conclude about its representation in the form of a digraph?

2. What is wrong with defining a digraph in such a way that there will be no elements of $V$ that do not appear in some ordered couple of $R$?

3. Could we proceed as follows: Leave the definition of digraph as is but introduce the notion of a *connected* digraph as one wherein every pair of nodes is a member of some diseg? (Hint: Examine Figure 18 in Section 5.1 carefully.)

4. In view of what you conclude from an examination of Figure 18 would it be better to define a connected digraph as one wherein every node belongs to some diseg?

5. How would *you* define a complete digraph?

6. Study the three digraphs below.

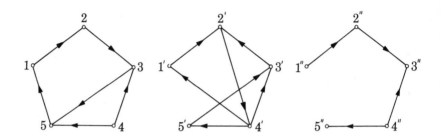

   (a) Are all three connected?
   (b) Are there any that are strongly connected?
   (c) Are there any that are complete?
   (d) Do you see the need for defining a type of connectivity somewhere between the two we have defined? How would you go about defining a notion of connectivity, call it *semistrongly connected*, that is somewhere between being simply connected and strongly connected? (Hint: Direct your attention to the paths between all node pairs in the above graphs.)

7. Recall how once we had introduced the notion of a set $S$ we very easily introduced the notion of a subset of $S$. How would you go about defining the notion of a subgraph of a given digraph $D$? (Hint: Evidently, it is not enough just to require that the nodes of the subgraph belong to a subset of the nodes of $D$.)

8. Is it possible for a subgraph of some connected graph to be disconnected?

9. Given a sketch of some digraph, we may either delete some nodes (along with those disegs entering and/or leaving them) or delete some disegs (leaving the nodes alone.) The digraph resulting from the latter operation on $D$ is called the *partial graph* of $D$. Define this notion and contrast it with the definition of a subgraph of $D$.

10. Sketch all the complete *ordinary* graphs of five nodes.

11. Which of the digraphs below (if any) are homeomorphic?

(Hint: Can you number the vertices of two or more of the digraphs in such a way that for every diseg $(n_i, n_j)$ appearing in one digraph $(n_i, n_j)$ also appears in the other?)

12. Are the two digraphs below homeomorphic?

Can you find two more distinct digraphs with 3 nodes and 4 disegs?

13. List all distinct (that is, omitting homeomorphisms) digraphs with 3 nodes and 3 disegs.

14. Find the answers to the following problems:

(a) $\begin{bmatrix} 3 & 2 \\ 4 & 1 \end{bmatrix} \times \begin{bmatrix} 5 & 1 \\ 3 & 2 \end{bmatrix} = ?$

(b) $\begin{bmatrix} 2 & 3 & -1 \\ 1 & -2 & 1 \\ -1 & -3 & 1 \end{bmatrix} \times \begin{bmatrix} x_1 \\ x_2 \\ x_3 \end{bmatrix} = ?$

(c) $\begin{bmatrix} a_{11} & a_{12} & a_{13} & a_{14} \\ a_{21} & a_{22} & a_{23} & a_{24} \\ a_{31} & a_{32} & a_{33} & a_{34} \\ a_{41} & a_{42} & a_{43} & a_{44} \end{bmatrix} \times \begin{bmatrix} 1 & 0 & 0 & 0 \\ 0 & 1 & 0 & 0 \\ 0 & 0 & 1 & 0 \\ 0 & 0 & 0 & 1 \end{bmatrix} = ?$

(Even though you're sure of your answer, see discussion in the Answers section.)

(d) Would you obtain a different result if you performed the last multiplication in reverse order?

(e) Can you think of a matrix that functions as an identity element with respect to matrix addition?

(f) $\begin{bmatrix} 3 & 1 \\ 6 & 2 \end{bmatrix} \times \begin{bmatrix} -1 & 3 \\ 3 & -9 \end{bmatrix} = ?$

15. If the matrix $A^{-1}$ is the inverse of $A$, what must be true about the product $A^{-1}A$ (or $AA^{-1}$)?

16. Solve the following equation for $X$:

$$AX = B,$$

where $A$, $X$, and $B$ are matrices. (*Caution:* The division, or ratio, of two matrices is not defined—that is, "there's no such thing.")

17.   Solve the following equation for $X$:

$$AX = I.$$

Can this equation always be solved for $X$?

18.   Find the inverse of

$$\begin{bmatrix} 1 & 2 \\ 3 & 4 \end{bmatrix}.$$

(Hint: Suppose some matrix

$$\begin{bmatrix} a & b \\ c & d \end{bmatrix}$$

is the inverse of the above matrix; if so, then it must be true that

$$\begin{bmatrix} 1 & 2 \\ 3 & 4 \end{bmatrix} \times \begin{bmatrix} a & b \\ c & d \end{bmatrix} = \begin{bmatrix} 1 & 0 \\ 0 & 1 \end{bmatrix},$$

from which you can find the values of $a$, $b$, $c$, and $d$.)

19.   Find the inverse of

$$\begin{bmatrix} 3 & 2 \\ 6 & 4 \end{bmatrix}.$$

20.   If

$$A = \begin{bmatrix} 1 & 3 \\ 2 & 4 \end{bmatrix}$$

find $A^2$.

21.   Does it make sense to speak of the square roots of a matrix? (Hint: Think of a specific, simple, known example, such as

$$\begin{bmatrix} 1 & 0 \\ 0 & 1 \end{bmatrix},$$

and ask what is the matrix that, when multiplied by itself, will give such a result?)

22.   If $AB = AC$, where $A$, $B$, and $C$ are matrices, can you in general conclude that $B = C$?

23.   Write the associated matrix for the following digraph and give the in-degree, out-degree, and the degree of each node.

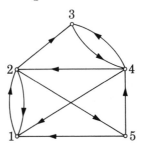

24. Construct a $5 \times 5$ matrix $M$ that will correspond to an asymmetric, transitive relation, and sketch the corresponding digraph. Give some examples of situations this kind of digraph might represent.

25. Find the square, $M^2$, of the above matrix $M$ and check the number of 2-diseg-long paths given by the matrix against those in the digraph.

26. Do the same for $M^3$.

27. An anthropologist is interested in the kinship relations $K$ (who is related to whom) and the friendship relations $F$ (who likes whom) in a group of people. Suppose he finds these to be as shown in the accompanying sketches,

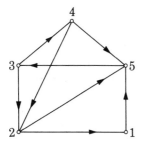 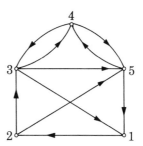

where the digraph on the left represents $K$ and the digraph on the right represents $F$.

(a) Find the digraph of the couples related by both friendship and kinship. (Hint: Find the associated matrix of each digraph and compute the product; this will represent $K \cap F$, which may be sketched from the product matrix.)

(b) Find the digraph of individuals related in *some* way (either by marriage or by friendship.)

(c) Find the digraph of people related by either blood or friendship, but *not* both.

# 6/ Probability Theory

## 6.1 Introduction

We bring our discussion to a close with an example of the application of some notions from set theory to the field of probability. The sets of probability theory are customarily referred to as *events*, and their elements are customarily spoken of as *sample points*. The statement, "A *set* is a *collection* of *elements*", becomes, in the language of probability theory, "An *event* is an *aggregate* of *sample points*." The aggregate of *all* sample points (the "universe") is called the *sample space*. Thus, the sample space when one die is tossed is

$$\mathfrak{U} = \{1, 2, 3, 4, 5, 6\}.$$

This is the set of *all logically possible* outcomes. The sample space for tossing a coin three times in a row is

$$\mathfrak{U} = \{\text{HHH, HHT, HTH, THH, HTT, THT, TTH, TTT}\}.$$

As an example of an event, $A$, we may consider (the subset) $A = \{\text{HHT, HTH, THH}\}$—that is, the event that, on tossing a coin three times in a row, exactly two heads will appear. Notice that the set shows the three possible ways in which this event can occur. The set $B = \{\text{HHH, HHT, HTH, THH}\}$ represents the event of obtaining at least two heads on three tosses of a coin. This event may also be described as the event of obtaining at most one tail on three tosses of a coin.* The event of three heads in a row may be represented

---

* Notice the precise (mathematical) use of such terms as "exactly," "at least," and "at most." The term "exactly," as used in mathematics, means *both* "at least" *and* "at most." To say "at most one" does not preclude the possibility that there may be *none*. But of course, "at least one" implies (mathematical) existence. Finally, the latter expression may be used even when there is only "at most" one, though "exactly one" would be more appropriate.

by the subset $C$ of $\mathfrak{U}$, where $C = \{\text{HHH}\}$: an event containing exactly one "point."

The event consisting of all points not contained in the event $A$, symbolized $\bar{A}$, is called the *complementary event* (or *negation*) of $A$. Thus in the case of $A$ as defined in the example above,

$$\bar{A} = \{\text{HHH, HTT, THT, TTH, TTT}\},$$

while for $B$, as defined above, $\bar{B} = \{\text{HTT, THT, TTH, TTT}\}$. Notice that $\bar{B} \subseteq \bar{A}$, owing, of course, to the fact that $A \subseteq B$ to begin with.

To express the fact that an event $A$ is "impossible"—that is, contains no sample points—the notation $A = \mathfrak{E}$ will be used. This notation will prove to be particularly useful (when compound events are considered) to define such a concept as *mutual exclusiveness* (described below).

In probability theory it is customary to represent intersection simply by juxtaposition, as in $AB$ (sometimes written $A \cdot B$). The union of two events, however, is customarily written $A \cup B$, as in the case of set theory.*

Just as the intersection or union of two sets is a set, so too the intersection or union of two events is an event—called a *compound event*. Thus, $AB$ represents the event "both $A$ and $B$ occur," while $A \cup B$ represents the event "either $A$ or $B$, or both, occur." If $A$ and $B$ exclude each other, then they have no points in common and the event $AB$ is impossible. This is symbolized $AB = \mathfrak{E}$; or verbally, "$A$ and $B$ are *mutually exclusive.*" For example, if the sample space is the set of all possibilities when a single die is tossed and $A = \{1\}$ while $B = \{2\}$, then $AB = \mathfrak{E}$, since both events cannot occur. Of course, $A \cup B \neq \mathfrak{E}$, since this represents the event of getting either a 1 or a 2.

Given any collection of events, $A, B, C, \ldots$, the aggregate of sample points that belong to all of these sets is denoted by $ABC, \ldots$, and may be called the simultaneous realization, or *intersection*, of events. The aggregate of sample points that belong to at least one of the given sets is denoted $A \cup B \cup C, \ldots$, and signifies the realization of at least one of the events; this aggregate may be called the *union* of the events. Thus, the union and the intersection of events are also events.

The notation $A \subseteq B$ means much the same here as in set theory, with the additional idea that $A \subseteq B$ is interpreted to mean that $A$ (materially) implies $B$. Alternatively, $B \supseteq A$ signifies that $B$ is implied by $A$. Note that if $A$ and $B$ are mutually exclusive events, then the occurrence of $A$ logically implies the nonoccurrence of $B$, and vice versa. Thus, $AB = \mathfrak{E}$ means the same as $A \subseteq \bar{B}$ or the same as $B \supseteq \bar{A}$.

The event $B - A$ contains those points that are in $B$ but not in $A$. This event may be symbolized, alternatively, by $\bar{A}B$. Notice that $\bar{A} = \mathfrak{U} - A$, here, just as in set theory.

---

* Many authors use $A + B$, but this may be confused with the plus sign of arithmetic.

## 6.2  Measures on Sets

Thus far we have been concerned, primarily, with matters of terminology—that is, with translating the language of set theory into the language of probability theory. But nothing has been said about the notion of "probability" as yet. Set theory supplies the foundation on which we build (as it does in so many other areas of mathematics). Indeed, all the relations of Section 3.6 (and many more besides) hold here, under the present interpretation.

The transition to probability theory is made by adopting the following convention or agreement:

> To each and every point of the sample space $\mathfrak{U}$ a nonnegative* number, called a *weight*, is assigned such that the sum of all the weights assigned will be 1.

Thus, weights, $w_i$, are numbers such that

$$0 \leq w_i \leq 1 \qquad \text{for every } w_i \tag{1}$$

and

$$\sum_{\mathfrak{U}} w_i = 1, \tag{2}$$

where the Greek sigma ($\Sigma$) means "sum of." The sum of the weights for some event $A \subseteq \mathfrak{U}$ will be symbolized by using a subscript $A$ on $\Sigma$ and, evidently,

$$\sum_A w_i \leqslant 1.$$

If $A = \mathfrak{U}$, of course, the sum of the weights has to be 1.

There are an unlimited number of ways of assigning these weights. One of the simplest ways, perhaps, is to assign equal weights to each point in the sample space. Thus, if there are $N$ points in the space, and we assign a weight of $1/N$ to each point, the sum of the weights will automatically be 1 as required. For example, with three points, we may assign a weight of $\frac{1}{3}$ to each, and $\frac{1}{3} + \frac{1}{3} + \frac{1}{3} = 1$. But we are at liberty to assign any other combination of weights, as long as they total 1—for example, $(\frac{1}{3}, \frac{2}{3}, 0)$ or $(\frac{2}{9}, \frac{4}{9}, \frac{3}{9})$. Considerations that determine the choice of weights will be dealt with shortly. The sum of the weights of the points in a set $A$ (that is, points making up the event $A$) is called the *probability measure*, or, simply, *measure*, $m(A)$, of that set. Evidently, the probability measure of the empty set $m(\mathfrak{E}) = 0$, the measure of the universal set $m(\mathfrak{U}) = 1$, and, in general, for $A \subseteq \mathfrak{U}$.

$$m(A) = \sum_A w_i \leqslant 1.$$

---

* We do not simply say "a positive number" here because we don't want to exclude zero; that is, both the positive numbers and zero are nonnegative (zero doesn't have a minus sign in front of it).

The three basic properties of a probability measure are:

(i) $m(A) \geqslant 0$, for any $A \subseteq \mathfrak{U}$—that is, the measure on a set is always a nonnegative number.

(ii) $m(\mathfrak{U}) = 1$.

(iii) For any two sets (events), $A \subset \mathfrak{U}$ and $B \subset \mathfrak{U}$, $m(A \cup B) = m(A) + m(B)$ only if $A \cap B = \mathfrak{E}$ (that is, only if $A$ and $B$ are disjoint).

Notice that the plus sign in property (iii) is the usual one of algebra, since the weights $m(A)$ and $m(B)$ are numbers.

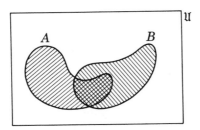

**Figure 22.** $m(A \cup B)$.

If two sets are not disjoint, as shown in Figure 22, then the weight of every element contained in both $A$ and $B$ simultaneously (that is, in the intersection, $A \cap B$) will have been counted twice in forming the sum $m(A) + m(B)$, as shown by the crosshatched region (Figure 22). Thus, in this case, the sum will be greater than $m(A \cup B)$ by an amount $m(A \cap B)$. Therefore, in general

$$m(A \cup B) = m(A) + m(B) - m(A \cap B). \tag{3}$$

If the events are disjoint, then, of course, $A \cap B = \mathfrak{E}$, and since $m(\mathfrak{E}) = 0$, therefore $m(A \cap B) = 0$ and the expression reduces to that given under property (iii) above.

## 6.3  Probabilities of Various Events

It is a simple matter, using the basic properties (i)–(iii), to show that, in fact, $m(\mathfrak{E}) = 0$, and this is why we omitted this fact from our list of *basic* properties. As a result of property (iii) we know that

$$m(A \cup \mathfrak{E}) = m(A) + m(\mathfrak{E}),$$

since $A$ and $\mathfrak{E}$ are obviously disjoint. But, from set theory, we know that

$$A \cup \mathfrak{E} = A.$$

Therefore,

$$m(A) = m(A) + m(\mathfrak{E}),$$

which means that $m(\mathfrak{E})$ must be zero. (Recall that these measures are ordinary real numbers and that the plus sign is the ordinary one of arithmetic.)

Another very important property is a simple matter to establish, and that is the fact that the measure on the complement of $A$, $m(\bar{A})$, may be found by simply subtracting the measure on $A$ from one: $1 - m(A) = m(\bar{A})$. We proceed to show this. Evidently,

$$m(A \cup \bar{A}) = m(A) + m(\bar{A}),$$

since $A$ and $\bar{A}$ are obviously disjoint. But, from set theory, we know that

$$A \cup \bar{A} = \mathfrak{U}.$$

By property (ii), therefore,

$$1 = m(A) + m(\bar{A})$$

or

$$m(\bar{A}) = 1 - m(A).$$

We could continue in this vein, developing an abstract "algebra of measures on discrete sets" (and indeed, generalize the notion of measure to the continuous case); however, this would take us too far afield. We content ourselves with associating the notion of "probability" with that of "measure" and then show the connection between this abstract definition of probability and the common notion usually arrived at in terms of examples involving the tossing of coins or throwing of dice. The probability of an event $A$, symbolized $p(A)$, is identified with the measure $m(A)$—that is, with the sum of the weights assigned to the points in $A$. Thus, from what has just been said, $p(\mathfrak{E}) = 0$, $p(\mathfrak{U}) = 1$, and

$$0 \leqslant p(A) \leqslant 1 \qquad \text{for all } A \subseteq \mathfrak{U}. \tag{4}$$

If, furthermore, $A, B, C, \ldots$ are pairwise disjoint events (subsets) of the sample space (universal set) $\mathfrak{U}$, then, evidently, since $m(\mathfrak{U}) = 1$,

$$p(A) + p(B) + p(C) + \cdots \leqslant 1. \tag{5}$$

Consider a sample space $\mathfrak{U}$, with $N$ points (Figure 23). Each point may be regarded as belonging to an event $E_i$ (subset) of the space $\mathfrak{U}$ (recall that a subset may contain just one point), and thus may be assigned a measure. We will call such events *point-events*. When there is just one point in the subset, the measure is, of course, the same as the weight of the point. With each of the $N$ measures $m(E_1), m(E_2), \ldots, m(E_N)$ may be associated one of the $N$ respective probabilities: $p(E_1), p(E_2), \ldots, p(E_N)$. Introducing the abbreviatory notation $p_1, p_2, \ldots, p_N$ for these probabilities, we may write equation (5) in the more compact form:

$$p_1 + p_2 + \cdots + p_N = \sum_{i=1}^{N} p_i = 1. \tag{6}$$

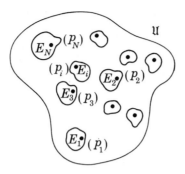

*Figure 23.* Sample space $\mathfrak{U}$ of point-events $E_i$.

The sum of the probabilities is set equal to 1 in this case, since the space has been "exhausted." Whenever $p(E_1) + p(E_2) + \cdots + p(E_N) = p(\mathfrak{U})$, where $p(\mathfrak{U}) = 1$, the events are said to be exhaustive. Thus, it is seen that in this case the weight, the measure, and the probability of an event all reduce to the same thing. A set of mutually exclusive, exhaustive events is evidently a partition of $\mathfrak{U}$.

When the event concerned (that is, the subset of $\mathfrak{U}$) contains more than one point, we have

$$p(A) = \sum_{E_i \in A} p(E_i). \tag{7}$$

That is, the probability of an event $A$ is equal to the sum of the probabilities (or weights) assigned to each point in $A$ (Figure 24).

The relations (4), (6), and (7) are basic to probability theory; some further relations of importance are:

$$p(A) + p(\bar{A}) = 1 \qquad \text{or} \qquad p(\bar{A}) = 1 - p(A), \tag{8}$$

$$p(A \cup B) = p(A) + p(B) - p(AB). \tag{9}$$

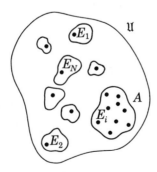

*Figure 24.* An event $A$ (subset of $\mathfrak{U}$) containing sample
points $E_i \in A$.

Equation (8) tells us that if we know the probability for the occurrence of an event, the probability that the event will not happen is found simply by subtracting the value of the former probability from 1, and equation (9) gives the probability for the occurrence of either $A$ or $B$, or of both.

These equations are readily justified by what has gone before. Equation (9), for example, is a direct consequence of equation (3). Recall that it is customary, in probability theory, to write $p(A \cap B)$—the probability of the joint occurrence of events $A$ and $B$—simply as $p(AB)$. If the events are disjoint—that is, mutually exclusive—so that $A \cap B = \mathfrak{E}$, then (and *only* then)*

$$p(A \cup B) = p(A) + p(B).$$

For example, the probability that a spade or a club will be drawn from a deck of cards is equal simply to the probability that a spade will be drawn plus

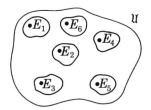

**Figure 25.** Sample space for rolling one die.

the probability that a club will be drawn (since *both* of these events can *not* happen on one draw). However, the probability that a spade or an ace (of any suit) will be drawn is *not* simply the sum of the probability that a spade will be drawn plus the probability that an ace will be drawn, since both these events could happen on one draw: the ace of spades could be drawn.

Let us consider a specific example of the application of the above results. Consider the set of all possible outcomes when a single die is rolled, $\mathfrak{U} = \{1, 2, 3, 4, 5, 6\}$. This set may be portrayed as in Figure 25. It is a sample space containing the (point) events $E_1, E_2, \ldots, E_6$, where we let $E_1$ stand for the event that a 1 turned up on the die, $E_2$ the event that a 2 turned up, and so on.

The first task is that of assigning a weight, or probability, to each one of the point-events $E_1, E_2, \ldots, E_6$. These numbers may be chosen at will, provided only that each is a nonnegative number between 0 and 1 such that they all total 1. Evidently, there is no reason for assigning a greater weight

---

* This relation is written by some authors as: $p(A + B) = p(A) + p(B)$. Such a usage is liable to lead to confusion since, whereas the plus sign in the right member of the equation is an arithmetic operator ($p(A)$ and $p(B)$ are, after all, *numbers* between 0 and 1), the plus sign in the left member stands for "or."

to the occurrence of one of these events than that assigned to the occurrence of any other event (assuming, of course, that the die is not "loaded"; if it is, then we need merely adjust the assignment of weights accordingly). Thus, the same weight or probability measure, is assigned to each point, namely, $\frac{1}{6}$: $p_1 = p_2 = \cdots = p_6 = \frac{1}{6}$. This is called the *equiprobable* measure (a different measure will be discussed shortly).

Once the weights, or probabilities, have been assigned to all the points of the sample space, the probabilities of the occurrence of various events are readily calculated. For example, suppose

$$A = \text{the event that an even number turns up,}$$

that is,

$$A = \{E_2, E_4, E_6\}, \text{ a subset of } \mathfrak{U}.$$

Then

$$p(A) = \sum_{E_i \in A} p(E_i) = p_2 + p_4 + p_6 = \tfrac{1}{6} + \tfrac{1}{6} + \tfrac{1}{6} = \tfrac{3}{6} = \tfrac{1}{2}.$$

Suppose

$$A = \text{the event that 1 turns up,}$$

and

$$B = \text{the event that 5 turns up,}$$

then the probability that either a 1 or a 5 will turn up when the die is tossed is

$$p(A \cup B) = p(A) + p(B) = \tfrac{1}{6} + \tfrac{1}{6} = \tfrac{2}{6} = \tfrac{1}{3},$$

since these events are mutually exclusive. This, of course, is quite different from asking for the probability of getting a 1 or a 5 in *two* tosses of a die, for here you might get both. Indeed, there are two ways in which this can happen: 1 on the first toss and 5 on the second, or vice versa.

In general, consider a space containing $n$ fixed points. If the weights are evenly distributed over the points (equiprobable measure), each receiving a weight of $1/n$, then some subset $A$, of $k$ points (Figure 26), has a measure equal to the sum of the weights of the $k$ points, namely, $k/n$.

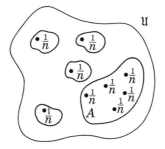

**Figure 26.** The equiprobable measure.

Consider now the tossing of a pair of dice in which interest is focused on the set or sample space of all possible sums from "snake-eyes" to "box-cars"; $\mathfrak{U} = \{2, 3, 4, 5, \ldots, 12\}$. In this case the equiprobable measure can *not* be used (that is, it would be incorrect to assign a weight of $\frac{1}{11}$ to each one of the eleven events in $\mathfrak{U}$) since, as is well known, certain events, such as a sum of 7, are much more likely to occur than others, such as a sum of 2.

The points representing the different events (that is, the different sums possible on throwing a pair of dice) may be conveniently arranged in the form of a lattice as shown in Figure 27 (for easier reading, not all the points are labeled). If we let $S$ be the set of possible outcomes when either die is tossed, then evidently $\mathfrak{U} = S \times S$ here. The first column of points depicts those events in which a 1 shows on one of the dice while either a 1, 2, 3, ..., or 6 appears on the other; the first row represents the reverse situation; and so on for other rows and columns in the lattice. One can pick out the various possible sums, and their manner of occurrence, by glancing down the diagonals as shown. For example, a sum of 10 may occur, as the result of the appearance of a 4 on one die and a 6 on the other, or vice versa, or, finally, as the result of the appearance of a 5 on each die.

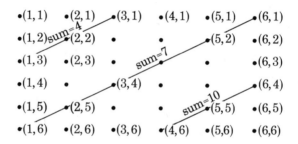

**Figure 27.** Possible outcomes on tossing a pair of dice (sample space).

As mentioned above, if the events of interest are *sums*, the equiprobable measure can *not* be used, but as far as each one of the 36 points in the lattice is concerned, no one point bears any more weight than any other. Thus a weight of $\frac{1}{36}$ may be assigned to each one of these points. The event "sum of 4" is thus assigned a measure of $\frac{3}{36}$ (equal to the sum of the weight), since this event can occur in three distinct ways (see Figure 27). The event "sum of 7" can occur in six distinct ways, each of weight $\frac{1}{36}$. The measure of this set (event) is, therefore, $\frac{6}{36} = \frac{1}{6}$. Proceeding in this way, the original space of 36 points may be "collapsed" into a space of 11 points, as shown in Figure 28. Each of these points may be considered an event with a certain weight (namely, the measures found above). Thus the event $E_2$ (that is, sum of 2) can occur in exactly one way, and so is assigned a weight of $\frac{1}{36}$ $E_3$ (sum of 3)

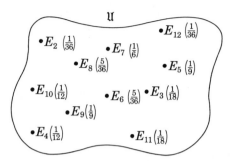

**Figure 28.** Sample space of sums when a pair of dice is tossed. (Each element in $\mathfrak{U}$—shown as a "point" for clarity—is a *set*; thus, for example, $E_4 = \{(1, 3), (2, 2), (3, 1)\}$. The numbers in parentheses are the measures on these sets.)

can occur in two ways and so is assigned a weight of $\frac{1}{36} + \frac{1}{36} = \frac{1}{18}$, and so on for the remaining ten events in $\mathfrak{U}$ (Figure 28).

Now that weights have been assigned to each of the points, the probabilities of various events are readily calculated. For example, let

$$A = \text{the sum of the dice is less than 6};$$

then

$$p(A) = p_2 + p_3 + p_4 + p_5$$
$$= \tfrac{1}{36} + \tfrac{2}{36} + \tfrac{3}{36} + \tfrac{4}{36} = \tfrac{10}{36} = \tfrac{5}{18}.$$

Again, let

$$A = \text{the sum is 7}$$

and

$$B = \text{the sum is 11};$$

the probability that a sum of 7 or one of 11 will occur is

$$p(A \cup B) = p(A) + p(B) = \tfrac{1}{6} + \tfrac{1}{18} = \tfrac{2}{9},$$

since these events are mutually exclusive. Notice that it is more probable that a sum less than 6 will occur on a given throw of the dice than that a sum of 7 or 11 will occur.

## 6.4  Conditional Probabilities

While the probability of the union of two events, $p(A \cup B)$, has been discussed, very little has been said about the probability of the intersection of two events $p(AB)$. It turns out to be convenient to consider first the notion of *conditional probability*, symbolized $p(A \mid B)$. This is the probability of the event *A given that event B occurred*. For example, if one die is tossed, the probability that, say, a 2 will show, $p(A) = \frac{1}{6}$. However, given that an even number occurred ($B$), the probability of a 2, $p(A \mid B)$, now is $\frac{1}{3}$. For if it is known that an even number occurred, the sample space $\mathfrak{U}$ is collapsed to $\{2, 4, 6\}$, each point having a weight of $\frac{2}{6} = \frac{1}{3}$.

In other words, if it is known that the event $B$ has occurred, the original set of *all* possibilities, $\mathfrak{U}$, has been reduced to the subset $B$. This subset now functions as a new "universe," and measures are now taken on subsets of $B$ (instead of on subsets of $\mathfrak{U}$). Of course, all of these subsets of $B$ are also (remain) subsets of $\mathfrak{U}$, and the measure on every one of them was already known before $B$ "occurred." However, since knowledge of $B$ cuts down on the number of possibilities, the new measure, $m'(X)$, on any set $X \subseteq B$ should be larger. We need to find the relation between this new measure and the old.

Knowing that the set of possibilities has been narrowed down to the event $B$ yields no new information about the subsets of $B$. However, suppose $E$ and $F$ are events such that the measure on $E$ happens to be, say, ten times as large as the measure on $F$; suppose $m(E) = 10m(F)$, when these measures are taken on $E$ and $F$ *considered as subsets* of $\mathfrak{U}$. Then, we should certainly require that the new measure, $m'$, preserve this result so that $m'(E) = 10m'(F)$ when the measures are taken on $E$ and $F$, considered, now, as *subsets of $B$*. This will be so if the measures on the subsets of $B$ are proportional to the original measures—that is, if $m'(X) = km(X)$ for any subset, $X$, of $B$. All that remains is to determine $k$, the constant of proportionality. Now, $m'(B) = 1$, since $B$ here plays the role of the universal set (of course, $m(B) \neq 1$). Thus

$$1 = m'(B) = km(B),$$

whence

$$k = \frac{1}{m(B)} \;;$$

therefore

$$m'(X) = \frac{m(X)}{m(B)},$$

where the measure $m'(X)$ is identified with the probability $p(A \mid B)$. Furthermore, since in this case $B$ functions in the capacity of a universal set, everything outside of $B$ (that is, all points of $\bar{B}$) has been eliminated. Thus, only that part of some set $A$ which is common to $B$ (only those events $A$ for which $B$ also occurred), namely, $A \cap B$, is to be considered. That is to say,

$$m(X) = m(A \cap B)$$

and therefore

$$p(A \mid B) = \frac{p(A \cap B)}{p(B)}. \tag{10}$$

This is another in our list of fundamental formulas.

A convenient device, sometimes, consists in representing the measures on sets by areas. Thus, the universe may be represented by a *unit square* and the measures on, say, a couple of sets (events) $A$ and $B$ may be represented by rectangular areas of unit bases and altitudes equal to $m(A)$ and $m(B)$—that is, strips of areas $1 \cdot m(A)$ and $1 \cdot m(B)$ as in the special cases shown in Figure 29.

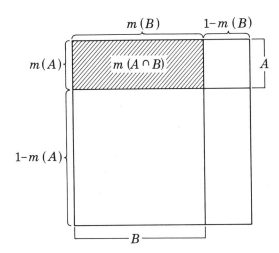

**Figure 29.** Measures represented by areas.

In Figure 29, the set $A$ is represented by the *horizontal* strip of base ("width") 1 and altitude ("height") $m(A)$, and the set $B$ is represented by the *vertical* strip of base ("height") 1 and altitude ("width") $m(B)$. The probabilities of these events may then be associated with the areas of the strips; that is, $p(A) = 1 \cdot m(A)$ and $p(B) = 1 \cdot m(B)$. Thus, for example, the probability $p(A)$, associated with the event $A$, is given by the *entire* area (part of it shown shaded) of the horizontal strip $A$, whereas the probability $p(A \cap B)$, of $A$ and $B$, is given by the *shaded* strip alone.

Notice that $m(A \cap B) = m(A) \cdot m(B)$ and that $p(A \cap B) = p(A) \cdot p(B)$ Whenever this special case holds, the two events are said to be *independent*. Writing this result in the form

$$\frac{p(A \cap B)}{p(B)} = p(A)$$

and inserting the result from equation (10), we find

$$p(A \mid B) = p(A).$$

That is to say, the probability of event $A$ given that event $B$ has occurred is the same as the probability of $A$, period. But this is precisely what we mean by saying $A$ and $B$ are independent. Thus a pair of events, $A$ and $B$, will be said to be independent if, and only if, $p(A \mid B) = p(A)$—or what amounts to the same thing, $p(B \mid A) = p(B)$, since it is arbitrary which event we choose to label "$A$" and which "$B$." In general, then, one would use equation (10) in the form:

$$p(AB) = p(A \mid B)p(B).$$

But if the events are *known* to be *independent*, as when a pair of dice is tossed and the number appearing on one die is independent of the number appearing on the other, we have the special case:

$$p(AB) = p(A) \cdot p(B).$$

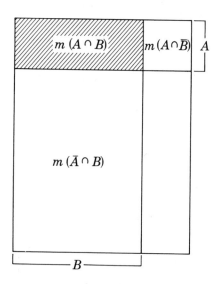

**Figure 30.** Measures represented by areas.

The general situation may be depicted in terms of the areas shown in Figure 30, where we require only that the over-all area of the entire figure does not exceed 1. The area of $A$ that is common to $B$ is labeled $m(A \cap B)$, and the area of $A$ that is not common to $B$ (that is, the area of $A$ that is outside of $B$, is labeled $m(A \cap \bar{B})$. Evidently,

$$m(B) = m(A \cap B) + m(\bar{A} \cap B).$$

The probability of $B$ given $A$ is represented by the ratio of the shaded area to the total area of $A$, so that

$$p(B \mid A) = \frac{m(A \cap B)}{m(A \cap B) + m(\bar{A} \cap B)}.$$

Similarly, the probability of $A$ given $B$ is represented by the ratio of the shaded area to the total area of, this time, $B$:

$$p(A \mid B) = \frac{m(A \cap B)}{m(A \cap B) + m(\bar{A} \cap B)} .$$

In terms of the previous terminology, this probability depends on the weight of the shaded region relative to the weight of the whole of $B$. If we know only that we are somewhere within the area of $B$ (that is, that event $B$ has occurred), then, evidently, the probability that we are also in $A$ will be greater the larger the proportion of $B$'s area that is taken over by $A$.

Notice that if the events $A$ and $B$ are known to be independent, then this situation reduces to the previous special case. Thus, for example,

$$p(B \mid A) = \frac{m(A \cap B)}{m(A \cap B) + m(A \cap \bar{B})} = \frac{m(A) \cdot m(B)}{m(A) \cdot m(B) + m(A) \cdot m(\bar{B})},$$

and if we are dealing with a unit square, so that $m(\bar{B}) = 1 - m(B)$,

$$p(B \mid A) = \frac{m(A) \cdot m(B)}{m(A) \cdot m(B) + m(A)[1 - m(B)]}$$

$$= \frac{m(A) \cdot m(B)}{m(A)} = m(B),$$

which says that $B$ is independent of $A$.

We give an example to bring out the distinction between independence and mutual exclusiveness. Let

$A =$ the event that a number greater than 3 will appear on one die,

$B =$ the event that a number less than 4 will appear on the other,

when a pair of dice is rolled. Since these events are *not* mutually exclusive, the probability that either a number less than 4 or a number greater than 3 will turn up is given by

$$p(A \cup B) = p(A) + p(B) - p(AB),$$

where $p(AB)$ is the probability of both events occurring. Since these two events *are*, however, independent,

$$p(AB) = p(A) \cdot p(B) = \tfrac{1}{2} \cdot \tfrac{1}{2} = \tfrac{1}{4},$$

and thus

$$p(A \cup B) = \tfrac{1}{2} + \tfrac{1}{2} - \tfrac{1}{4} = \tfrac{3}{4}.$$

As another example, consider a well-shuffled deck of 52 ordinary playing cards from which cards are to be drawn. This is a case of the equiprobable measure (since any one card is as likely to be drawn as any other) and so a weight of $\tfrac{1}{52}$ is assigned to each card. Since there are four aces in the deck,

$$p(\text{drawing an ace}) = \tfrac{4}{52} = \tfrac{1}{13},$$

and, since there are thirteen spades,

$$p(\text{drawing a spade}) = \tfrac{13}{52} = \tfrac{1}{4}.$$

Suppose that after a card is picked it is announced to be an ace; what is the probability that it is a spade? Obviously, the same as before, namely, $\tfrac{1}{4}$, since these two events are independent. The only information conveyed by this announcement is that the probability space is smaller than $\mathfrak{U} = \{52$ cards$\}$. The information that the card is an ace reduces the space to $\{H, D, C, S\}$, where $H$ stands for ace of hearts, $D$ for ace of diamonds, and so on; each point in this subset has a weight of $\tfrac{1}{4}$. Notice that, here, $p(\text{spade}) = p(\text{space} \mid \text{ace})$. If, however, three aces have already been removed from the deck, leaving only the ace of spades (among the 49 remaining cards), then the probability that the next draw results in ace, $p(\text{ace}) = \tfrac{1}{49}$, while, for example, $p(\text{ace} \mid \text{club}) = 0$ (since only the ace of *spades* remains in the deck), so that, in this case, $p(\text{ace}) \neq p(\text{ace} \mid \text{club})$; that is, the two events are not independent.

Suppose two cards are arbitrarily selected from the deck; what is the probability they are both aces? Let

$A$ = the event that the first card drawn is an ace,

$B$ = the event that the second card drawn is an ace.

Evidently, $p(A) = \tfrac{4}{52}$, as before. However, after the first card is drawn, there are only 51 cards remaining in the deck; furthermore, *if* the first card drawn *were* an ace, there would be only three aces left in the deck. Thus, the probability that the second card drawn is an ace, *conditional on the first card's having been an ace*, is

$$p(A \mid B) = \tfrac{3}{51}.$$

Therefore,

$$p(AB) = p(A) \cdot p(A \mid B) = (\tfrac{4}{52})(\tfrac{3}{51}) = \tfrac{1}{221}$$

—a fairly improbable occurrence! If the first ace is replaced (and the deck reshuffled), then, of course,

$$p(AB) = p(A)p(B) = (\tfrac{4}{52})(\tfrac{4}{52}) = \tfrac{1}{169}.$$

Let us turn, now, to a somewhat more heuristic example. Suppose we are given two boxes, I and II, each containing a different known mixture of white ($W$) and red ($R$) poker chips (as shown in Figure 31), and that a drawing is to be made from one of these boxes. Suppose, further, that one box is just as likely to be picked as the other (for example, we might toss a coin, choosing Box I if it comes up heads, but choosing II if it comes up tails). Then, on the basis of the information given so far, it is appropriate to assign the initial, or prior, probabilities: $p(\text{I chosen}) = p(\text{II chosen}) = \tfrac{1}{2}$; these

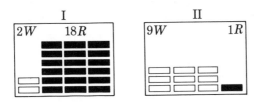

**Figure 31.** A pair of boxes containing different mixtures of red and white poker chips.

are called *a priori* probabilities. Given the additional information that a white chip was drawn, one might inquire after its chance of having been drawn from box I. The probability that I was chosen given that the chip drawn is white, $p(I \mid W)$, is called the *a posteriori* probability. Since the second box has by far the greater majority of white chips, the information that the chip drawn is $W$ would incline one to bet that Box II was chosen.* But suppose, now, that it is known that Box I is invariably selected 99 out of 100 times, so that $p(I \text{ chosen}) = \frac{99}{100}$ and $p(II \text{ chosen}) = \frac{1}{100}$. In this case, one would be more inclined to "guess" that the $W$ chip came from the first box.

To illustrate the use of formula (10), assume it is known in advance that eight times out of ten Box I will be picked as the one from which to draw a chip (and, hence, two out of ten times Box II will be chosen). Given that the chip drawn is $W$, what is the probability it came from the first box? Notice that the (over-all) probability of drawing a $W$ chip, $p(W)$, is given by the sum of the probabilities of drawing it from Box I plus that of drawing it from Box II. Using equation (10), we find†

$$p(I \mid W) = \frac{p(I \cap W)}{p(W)} = \frac{p(I)p(W \mid I)}{p(W)}$$

$$= \frac{\left(\frac{8}{10}\right)\left(\frac{2}{20}\right)}{\left(\frac{8}{10}\right)\left(\frac{2}{20}\right) + \left(\frac{2}{10}\right)\left(\frac{9}{10}\right)}$$

$$= \frac{\left(\frac{16}{200}\right)}{\left(\frac{52}{200}\right)} = \frac{4}{13}.$$

Furthermore, the probability that the white chip came from Box II is, evidently,

$$p(II \mid W) = 1 - \frac{4}{13} = \frac{9}{13}.$$

---

* This is made obvious in the case in which the first box contains no white chips. In that case, the additional information that the chip drawn is $W$ makes it certain that the box chosen was the second. Notice that the *a priori* probability of choosing the second (or first) box is still $\frac{1}{2}$.

† Some readers may recognize this result as an application of the famous Bayes' formula.

The *a priori* probability of choosing, say, Box II is only 0.20 (that is, 2 out of 10 times); however, after it is known that a $W$ chip has been drawn, this additional knowledge increases the probability to about 0.69 (which is the *a posteriori* probability that Box II was chosen, given that the chip drawn is $W$). Notice that the over-all probability of a $W$ chip, no matter whether from Box I or Box II, is

$$p(W) = p(W \mid \text{I})p(\text{I}) + p(W \mid \text{II})p(\text{II}).$$

## 6.5   Discrete Probability Distributions

Let $X$ be a variable that can assume a set of discrete values $x_1, x_2,$ $x_3, \ldots, x_n$ with respective probabilities $p_1, p_2, \ldots, p_n$, where $p_1 + p_2 + \cdots + p_n = 1$. In that case, we will say that a *discrete probability distribution* has been defined for $X$. For example, $X$ might represent the various possible sums when a pair of dice is tossed. The discrete values that $X$ may assume and the probabilities with which $X$ takes on these values are shown in the following table:

| $X$ | 2 | 3 | 4 | 5 | 6 | 7 | 8 | 9 | 10 | 11 | 12 |
|---|---|---|---|---|---|---|---|---|---|---|---|
| $p(X)$ | $\frac{1}{36}$ | $\frac{2}{36}$ | $\frac{3}{36}$ | $\frac{4}{36}$ | $\frac{5}{36}$ | $\frac{6}{36}$ | $\frac{5}{36}$ | $\frac{4}{36}$ | $\frac{3}{36}$ | $\frac{2}{36}$ | $\frac{1}{36}$ |

The function $p(X)$, which takes on the respective values $\frac{1}{36}, \frac{2}{36}, \ldots, \frac{1}{36}$ as $X$ takes on the values $2, 3, \ldots, 12$, is called the *probability function* of $X$. Since $X$ assumes its values $(2, 3, \ldots, 12)$ with certain probabilities, it is called a *random* or *stochastic* (from Greek, meaning "chance") *variable*. The probability distribution exhibited in the table above may also be displayed in the form of a graph, as shown in Figure 32. (It is customary, when

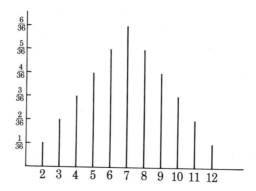

**Figure 32.** Graph of the probability distribution for the possible sums when a pair of dice is tossed.

making such graphs, to draw vertical lines to the points whose heights give the probabilities.)

### 6.5.1 The Binomial Probability Distribution

We will now consider a particular type of discrete probability distribution called the binomial probability distribution, that has been found to be useful for studying a certain class of chance phenomena in which exactly one of two possible events may occur: for example, a "success" or a "failure." Thus, in tossing a coin, a head might be considered a "success" and a tail a "failure," or a "yes" answer on a questionnaire might be considered a "success" and a "no" a "failure," and so on.

In particular, the binomial distribution applies to those situations in which the occurrence, on a given trial, of exactly one of two mutually exclusive events is independent of what occurs on any other trial and where the probability remains constant from trial to trial. The tossing of a coin is typical of the class of phenomena governed by the binomial distribution:

(i) there are exactly two possible mutually exclusive outcomes on each trial (toss);

(ii) the outcome on any one trial (toss) is independent of the outcome on any other trial (toss);

(iii) the probability of a particular outcome (say, $H$) remains constant from trial to trial (toss to toss); for example, the probability of H when a fair coin is tossed the same way on each trial remains at $\frac{1}{2}$ from toss to toss.

As regards the last property, the coin may be lopsided so that, say, $p(\mathrm{H}) = \frac{1}{3}$. All that is required is that the probability of H, $p(\mathrm{H})$, remain the same from trial to trial.

When a series of trials satisfies the properties (i)–(iii) above, the trials are referred to as *Bernoulli trials*. The binomial distribution thus applies only to the case of such Bernoulli trials.

We now derive an expression for this distribution. But first, let us recall some results from elementary algebra:

$$(p + q)^2 = p^2 + 2pq + q^2,$$
$$(p + q)^3 = p^3 + 3p^2q + 3pq^2 + q^3,$$

and, in general,

$$(p + q)^n = p^n + np^{n-1}q + \frac{n(n - 1)}{2!} p^{n-2}q^2$$
$$+ \frac{n(n - 1)(n - 2)}{3!} p^{n-3}q^3 + \cdots + npq^{n-1} + q^n. \quad (1)$$

(You will find the latter formula in any first-year college algebra text under the heading "Binomial Theorem.")

Now suppose a biased coin with $p =$ probability of $H = \frac{1}{3}$ and $q =$ probability of $T = \frac{2}{3}$ (notice that $p = 1 - q$, as it should) is tossed three times in a row. The various events that may occur and the probabilities associated with each are displayed in the table below:

| Event | Probability of Event | |
|-------|---------------------|---|
| HHH | $p^3 = (1/3)^3 = 1/27$ | |
| HHT | $p^2q = (1/3)^2(2/3) = 2/27$ | |
| HTH | $pqp = (1/3)(2/3)(1/3) = 2/27$ | $3p^2q$ |
| THH | $qp^2 = (2/3)(1/3)^2 = 2/27$ | |
| TTH | $q^2p = (2/3)^2(1/3) = 4/27$ | |
| THT | $qpq = (2/3)(1/3)(2/3) = 4/27$ | $3pq^2$ |
| HTT | $qp^2 = (1/3)(2/3)^2 = 4/27$ | |
| TTT | $q^3 = (2/3)^3 = 8/27$ | |

Notice from the table that the expression $p^2q$ (or some equivalent, such as $qp^2$ and $pqp$) occurs three times. Thus, the sum of all the expressions may be written in the form

$$p^3 + 3p^2q + 3pq^2 + q^3,$$

which happens to be the expansion of $(p + q)^3$. Since $q = 1 - p, p + q = 1$, of course, and so $(p + q)^3 = 1$ as well. Notice that the sum above, which in this example works out to be

$$\tfrac{1}{27} + 3 \times \tfrac{2}{27} + 3 \times \tfrac{4}{27} + \tfrac{8}{27},$$

adds up to one, as it should. (Some one of the events in the table *must* occur—that is, the probability that either HHH, or HHT, or HTH, . . . , or TTT occurs is one.)

Here is what has been discovered. If a coin is tossed three times in a row with a probability of heads equal to $p$ and a probability of tails equal to $q = 1 - p$, then the first term in the expansion of $(p + q)^3$ gives the probability of three heads, the next term the probability of two heads, the next the probability of one head, and the last term gives the probability of no heads.

In general, if $p$ is the probability of a "success" on a given trial and $q$ is the probability of a "failure" on a given trial in a sequence of Bernoulli trials, then the first term, $p^n$, in the expansion of $(p + q)^n$ gives the probability of $n$ successes in $n$ trials; the next term gives the probability of $n - 1$ successes in $n$ trials; the next, the probability of $n - 2$ successes in $n$ trials; until, finally, the last term, $q^n$, gives the probability of no successes (that is, $n$

failures) in $n$ trials. For example, in a series of 5 trials, we have, using formula (1) above:

$$(p + q)^5 = p^5 + 5p^4q + \frac{5 \times 4}{1 \times 2}p^3q^2 + \frac{5 \times 4 \times 3}{1 \times 2 \times 3}p^2q^3$$

$$+ \frac{5 \times 4 \times 3 \times 2}{1 \times 2 \times 3 \times 4} + q^5$$

$$= p^5 + 5p^4q + 10p^3q^2 + 10p^2q^3 + 5pq^4 + q^5,$$

from which we read immediately that, for example, the probability of 2 successes is $10p^2q^3$. Notice, furthermore, that the probability of *at least* two successes may be found at once from $p^5 + 5p^4q + 10p^3q^2 + 10p^2q^3$; the probability of at least three successes from $p^5 + 5p^4q + 10p^3q^2$; and so on.

It can be shown (see any first-year college algebra text) that the formula for the term involving $p^r$, in the expansion of $(p + q)^n$, is

$$\frac{n!}{r!\,(n - r)!}p^rq^{n-r}.$$

For example, the term involving $p^3$, in the expansion of $(p + q)^5$, is

$$\frac{5!}{3!\,(5 - 3)!}p^3q^{5-3} = \frac{5!}{3!\,2!}p^3q^2$$

$$= \frac{1 \times 2 \times 3 \times 4 \times 5}{1 \times 2 \times 3 \times 1 \times 2}p^3q^2$$

$$= 10p^3q^2,$$

and, of course, this term gives the probability of exactly 3 successes in 5 trials.

Another way of looking at this is as follows. Let $S$ stand for success and $F$ for failure, then one possible way in which 3 successes can occur in 5 trials is: $SFSFS$. If $p$ is the probability of a success (for example, H appearing when a coin is tossed) and $q$ is the probability of failure (T appearing), then

$$p(SFSFS) = p \cdot q \cdot p \cdot q \cdot p = p^3q^2.$$

But, by the same token, the probability for some different pattern of 3 successes and 2 failures, such as $FSSFS$, is

$$p(FSSFS) = q \cdot p \cdot p \cdot q \cdot p = p^3q^2.$$

—the same result as before. In general, the probability of $r$ successes and $n - r$ failures, in some definite order, is given by: $p^rq^{n-r}$. So the question now resolves itself to discovering how many different patterns are possible on $r$ successes ($S$'s) and $n - r$ failures ($F$'s). This amounts to finding the number of combinations of two things ($S$'s and $F$'s) taken $n$ at a time (where $n$ = the number of trials). You will recall that the formula for this (see Exercises 3 through 7, Chapter 2) is

$$C(n, r) = \frac{n!}{r!\,(n - r)!}\,.$$

Thus, the probability of exactly $r$ successes in $n$ trials, regardless of the order, is

$$\frac{n!}{r!\,(n - r)!}\,p^r q^{n-r},$$

or, more compactly,

$$B(r; n, p) = C(n, r)p^r q^{n-r}. \tag{2}$$

gives the formula for finding the probability of exactly $r$ successes in a sequence of $n$ Bernoulli trials, when the probability of a success is $p$ and the probability of a failure is $q = 1 - p$. The function $B$ (notice that it is a function of $r$, of $n$, and of $p$) is called the binomial (probability) distribution. (We use $B$ for "binomial"; we could as well have expressed the function as $F(r; n, p)$—no other significance attaches to the use of $B$.)

Notice that our interest is not so much in the results of individual trials but, rather, in the results of a set of $n$ trials taken as a whole. That is to say, we are primarily interested in the number $r$ of $S$'s in a sequence of $n$ symbols of the type $SFSFFS, \ldots$, without regard to their order. One "experiment" thus consists of $n$ trials, and a single event consists of a sequence of $r$ successes (or $S$'s) and $n - r$ failures (or $F$'s) without regard to order. Every possible outcome of an experiment (for example, 10 tosses of a coin) will have a definite value $r$ (for example, the outcome "no heads in 10 tosses" has the value $r = 0$; the outcome "one head in 10 tosses" has the value $r = 1$; ... ; the outcome "ten heads in 10 tosses" has the value $r = 10$—assuming, of course, that a head is counted as a "success"). Thus we may regard any particular $r$ as the value of a random variable $R$. (Recall our remarks at the beginning of Section 6.5.)

### 6.5.2 The Geometric Distribution

Whereas the random variable $R$ in the binomial distribution is the number of successes in $n$ Bernoulli trials, the random variable $N$ in the case of the geometric distribution is the number of trials required to obtain the first success in a sequence of Bernoulli trials. The class of phenomena to which the geometric distribution applies are sometimes called waiting-time phenomena, since the events preceding a success (or a failure for that matter) may be considered as the waiting time for the occurrence of a success.

Evidently, if a success does not occur until the $n$th trial, the preceding $n - 1$ trials must have been failures. If the probability of a success on any trial is constant and equal to $p$, then the probability of $n - 1$ consecutive failures is evidently equal to $q^{n-1}$. This may also be found from the binomial distribution (equation (2)) to be:*

$$B(0; n - 1, p) = \frac{(n - 1)!}{0! \, (n - 1)!} \, p^0 q^{n-1} = q^{n-1}.$$

Thus, the probability of zero successes on $n - 1$ trials (that is, $n - 1$ consecutive failures) followed by a success on the $n$th trial is $pq^{n-1}$, and we write

$$G(n; p) = pq^{n-1}. \tag{3}$$

This formula is used to find the probability that it will take $n$ trials to achieve *one* success—which, of course, means that the success occurs on the $n$th trial. Alternatively, it can be used to find the probability that a *failure* will occur on the $n$th trial (preceded by $n - 1$ successes); one need only let $p =$ probability of *failure*, then $1 - q =$ probability of success.

As an example of the application of formula (3), consider a spacecraft that has a probability of 0.90 of successfully accomplishing a space mission, such as "flying within 1,000 miles of Mars." Then, the probability that a success (a Mars flyby, within 1,000 miles) will occur on, say, the third launch (that is, the probability that it will take three tries to obtain one success) is given by

$$G(3; 0.9) = 0.9 \times (0.1)^2 = 0.009$$

—a fairly small number, so the chances are good that it will not take that many tries. Another way of looking at this is to compute the probability of one success in three tries:

$$G(1; 0.9) + G(2; 0.9) + G(3; 0.9)$$
$$= 0.9 \times (0.1)^0 + (0.9) \times (0.1) + 0.9 \times (0.1)^2$$
$$= 0.9 + 0.09 + 0.009 = 0.999,$$

which is pretty close to certainty.

### 6.5.3 The Pascal Distribution

Suppose, instead of being interested in the number of trials to obtain the first success, we are interested in the number of trials to obtain $r$ successes—that is, in the probability that it will take exactly $n$ trials to achieve $r$ successes. This problem leads to the *Pascal distribution*, the formula for which is

$$P(n; r, p) = \frac{(n - 1)!}{(r - 1)! \, (n - r)!} \, p^r q^{n-r}. \tag{4}$$

* Recall that 0! is defined as equal to 1. The algebraic fact that $x^0 = 1$ is also used here.

The appearance of $p^r q^{n-r}$ in this formula is justified in exactly the same way as discussed under the derivation of the binomial distribution. The expression may be written more compactly in the form

$$P(n; r, p) = C(n - 1, r - 1)p^r q^{n-r}, \tag{5}$$

as can be seen by substituting $n - 1$ for $n$ and $r - 1$ for $r$ in

$$C(n, r) = \frac{n!}{r!\,(n - r)!}.$$

This result is entirely reasonable—for, since the $r$th success must occur on the $n$th (last) trial, the possible number of patterns of $S$'s and $F$'s, here, depends on the arrangement of the prior $r - 1$ success within the preceding $n - 1$ trials.

Notice, finally, that when we let $r = 1$ in formula (5), we get

$$P(n; r, p) = C(n - 1, 0)pq^{n-1}$$

$$= \frac{(n - 1)!}{0!\,(n - 1)!}\, pq^{n-1} = pq^{n-1}.$$

In other words, the $P$-distribution reduces to the $G$-distribution, as it should.

## 6.6 Summary

The basic concepts and formulas of this chapter are summarized below. As in all the previous chapters, the primary objective has been to acquaint you with some fundamental terminology and concepts and to provide you with some practice in using the new material. The distributions discussed above are the most common; there are, of course, many others. Furthermore, everything in this chapter deals with discrete probabilities. The study of continuous probability distributions, for which an intimate knowledge of the calculus is required, forms almost a separate subject matter.

We began the chapter with the notion of a certain universal set called the *sample space* and certain subsets of this space called *events*. The elements of the space, in this case, are called *sample points*. The sample space is the set of all logically possible outcomes for some phenomenon, such as repeated tosses of a die for which the sample space is $\{1, 2, 3, 4, 5, 6\}$. An event (subset) might consist of a single element (for example, $\{2\}$ represents the event of a 2 showing), several elements ($\{2, 4, 6\}$ represents the event of an even number showing), or even, no elements (such as the event of getting a ten when a single die is tossed; this event is represented by the null set).

The event $\bar{E}$ consisting of all points not belonging to $E$ is called the *complementary event* when the sample space is given, in analogy with ordinary set theory.

Since events are sets, it is sensible to speak of the union and intersection of events; these events are called *compound events*. The union of a collection of events signifies the realization of at least one of the events; the intersection signifies the simultaneous realization of all the events.

When the intersection of a pair of events is empty ($E_1 \cap E_2 = \mathfrak{E}$), the events are said to be *mutually exclusive*.

The notion of *probability measure* on a set (event) was introduced by assigning a nonnegative number, called a *weight*, to each point of the sample space ("universe") $\mathfrak{U}$ in such a way that the sum of all the weights is 1. The measure $m(A)$ on any $A \subseteq \mathfrak{U}$ is found by simply totaling the weights of all the points belonging to $A$. The basic properties of a measure are:

(1) $m(A) \geqslant 0$ for any $A \subseteq \mathfrak{U}$.

(2) $m(\mathfrak{U}) = 1$.

(3) If $A \subseteq \mathfrak{U}$ and $B \subseteq \mathfrak{U}$, then $m(A \cup B) = m(A) + m(B)$ only when $A \cap B = \mathfrak{E}$.

The *probability* $p(A)$ of an event is given by the measure, $m(A)$, on the set $A \subseteq \mathfrak{U}$. Thus, $p(A)$ is a nonnegative number such that $p(A) + p(B) + p(C) + \cdots \leqslant 1$, when $A, B, C, \ldots \subseteq \mathfrak{U}$ (that is, when $A, B, C, \ldots$ are events in $\mathfrak{U}$).

Some rules for operating with these probabilities are as follows.

The probability that either one of two (possibly both) events occurs is found from

$$p(A \cup B) = p(A) + p(B) - p(A \cap B),$$

which reduces to

$$p(A \cup B) = p(A) + p(B)$$

*when the two events are mutually exclusive.*

The *conditional probability* of one event, given the occurrence of another event, is found from

$$p(A \mid B) = \frac{p(A \cap B)}{p(B)}.$$

$p(A \mid B)$ is the probability of $A$, given that $B$ has occurred. The denominator is the probability of $B$ regardless of whether $A$ occurs or not; it may therefore be found by evaluating

$$p(B \mid A)p(A) + p(B \mid \bar{A})p(\bar{A}).$$

The numerator is the probability of both events; thus the probability that both of two events occur may be found using

$$p(A \cap B) = p(B)p(A \mid B).$$

When the events $A$ and $B$ are *independent*, we write $p(A \mid B) = p(A)$ or, equivalently, $p(B \mid A) = p(B)$. Thus, the formula for finding the probability of the joint occurrence of a pair of events, *when the two events are independent*, is given by

$$p(A \cap B) = p(A)p(B).$$

Since, obviously, $p(A \cap B) = p(B \cap A)$, we may write

$$p(B)p(A \mid B) = p(A)p(B \mid A),$$

from which

$$p(A \mid B) = \frac{p(A)p(B \mid A)}{p(B)}.$$

This formula is usually called the Bayes rule. On the right side, $p(A)$ is referred to as the *a priori* probability; it is the probability of $A$ prior to any knowledge about $B$. On the left, $p(A \mid B)$ is referred to as the *a posteriori* probability of $A$: the probability of $A$ given that $B$ has occurred. The formula affords a means of revising our knowledge concerning the probability of the occurrence of an event $A$ given some additional information, to the effect that a second event $B$ occurred ($A$ not being independent of $B$). The over-all probability of $B$ regardless of whether or not $A$ occurs must be known, as well as the probability of $B$ given $A$.

Finally, the notion of a *random variable* was introduced and several *discrete* probability distributions were discussed.

The binomial distribution,

$$B(r; n, p) = C(n, r)p^r q^{n-r},$$

is used for finding the probability of $r$ successes in a sequence of $n$ Bernoulli trials.

The geometric distribution,

$$G(n; p) = pq^{n-1},$$

is used for finding the probability that $n$ trials are required for one success (or one failure) in a sequence of Bernoulli trials.

The Pascal distribution,

$$P(n; r, p) = C(n - 1, r - 1)p^r q^{n-r},$$

is used to find the probability that it will take $n$ trials to achieve $r$ successes.

# EXERCISES

1. In some elementary developments the following definition of a "probability function" forms a point of departure for probability theory:

   Given a sample space $\mathfrak{U}$, and a family $\mathfrak{F}$ of events (subsets) in $\mathfrak{U}$, a *probability function* assigns to each event $E$ in $\mathfrak{F}$ a real number $p(E)$, called the *probability* of event $E$, such that:

(i) $p(E) \geqslant 0$ for all $E \subseteq \mathfrak{F}$,

(ii) $p(\mathfrak{U}) = 1$,

(iii) $p(E_1 \cup E_2 \cup \cdots E_n) = p(E_1) + p(E_2) + \cdots + p(E_n)$ whenever the $E_i$ are pairwise disjoint (that is, $E_i \cap E_j = \mathfrak{E}$ for every pair of events) and denumerable. (This last axiom just says that the probability of the union of a countable number of mutually exclusive events is equal to the sum of their separate probabilities.)

Using anything you have learned from *set theory*, and using one or more of the above axioms alone (which, note, say nothing about measures), (a) prove that $p(E) \leqslant 1$, always, for any event (set) $E$. (Hint: Suppose there could be some event $E$ for which $p(E) > 1$, can you derive a contradiction to one of the axioms above? Prove first that $p(E) + p(\overline{E}) = 1$; notice that this also establishes the fact that $p(\overline{E}) = 1 - p(E)$.) (b) Prove that $p(\mathfrak{E}) = 0$, where $\mathfrak{E}$ is the null set.

2. How do you conclude from the *set-theoretic* fact that, for any $E \subseteq \mathfrak{U}$, $E \cup \overline{E} = \mathfrak{U}$ the probability result that $p(E \cup \overline{E}) = p(\mathfrak{U})$? Can you simply multiply both sides of the first equality by $p$? (Of course not!) Does it help any to say you are "taking the probability of both sides of the equality"? What does *that* mean? How *do* you get from

$$E \cup \overline{E} = \mathfrak{U}$$

to

$$p(E \cup \overline{E}) = p(\mathfrak{U})?$$

Think about this for a while!

3. If $A \subseteq B$, $p(B - A) = ?$ Can you *prove* your result?

4. If $A \subseteq B$, what can you conclude about the relative magnitudes of $p(A)$ and $p(B)$—for example, is $p(A) > p(B)$? Recall the statement at the end of Section 6.1 that when $A$ and $B$ are events, we interpret $A \subseteq B$ to signify that $B$ is implied by $A$—that is, $A$ cannot happen without $B$ also happening. (Hint: Use the previous result.)

5. For any pair of events, what is the relative magnitude of $p(A \cup B)$ versus $p(A \cap B)$? (Hint: Recall that the first expression is the probability that both events occur while the second is the probability that either one occurs.) Can you *prove* it—assuming your answer is correct, of course? (Hint: Use the result in Exercise 4 plus the fact, from set theory, that, if $A \subseteq B$ then $A \cap B = A$ and $A \cup B = B$.)

6. Recall the formula $p(A \cup B) = p(A) + p(B) - p(A \cap B)$. Can you derive the formula for $p(A \cup B \cup C)$? (Hint: Look upon it as $p[A \cup (B \cup C)]$ and use the previous formula.)

7. Is $m(A \cap B) > m(A) + m(B)$ or what? (Hint: Examine equation (3) in Section 6.2.)

8. Recall the formula $p(A \cap B) = p(A) \cdot p(B \mid A)$. Can you derive the formula for $p(A \cap B \cap C)$?

9.  Three people write their names on separate slips of paper and mix the slips up in a hat. What is the probability that each person will draw his own name-slip?

10. An urn contains 10 red, 40 white, and 50 blue chips. Each time a chip is withdrawn it is replaced and the urn shaken well before the next draw. What is the probability that in three draws:
    (a) No white chip appears?
    (b) Three white chips appear?
    (c) A red, a white, and a blue chip appear, in that order?
    (d) A red, a white, and a blue chip appear in any order?
    (e) At least one white chip is drawn?
    Assume $p(R) = 0.10$, $p(W) = 0.40$, and $p(B) = 0.50$.

11. A "fair" coin is tossed 10 times in a row. What is the probability of getting:
    (a) At least one tail?
    (b) Exactly one tail?
    (c) At most one tail?
    Assume $p(H) = p(T) = \frac{1}{2}$.

12. An urn contains 12 well-mixed chips numbered from 1 through 12. If a chip is drawn at random, what is the probability that the number drawn is a divisor of 12?

13. In the problem above, what is the probability that the number drawn is a multiple of either 3 or 4?

14. A card is drawn from a well-shuffled deck of 52 cards. What is the probability that it is:
    (a) Either black or a Jack?
    (b) Red or a spade?
    (c) A spade or a diamond?

15. Three boxes each contain a couple of marbles. Both marbles in one box are red, both in another box are blue, and the third box contains a blue and a red marble. You are told that one of the boxes was selected purely arbitrarily and a red marble happened to be arbitrarily drawn from it. What is the probability that the second marble in the box is also red?

16. Owing to poor preparation or whatever other factors, it has been found that in the past, on the average, only 50 per cent of the students entering a certain course have managed to get a passing grade. Rather than admitting indiscriminately all students who applied for the course, it was soon decided to admit only those candidates who first passed a qualifying test. During the try-out it was found that only 20 per cent of the students who failed the course could pass the qualifying test initially, whereas of the students who passed the course, 70 per cent also passed the qualifying test beforehand.
    (a) If this test is to be used for future placement and only a student passing it is to be admitted to the course, what is the probability that such a student will pass the course? (Hint: The *a priori* probability of passing the course is 0.50; you are seeking the *a posteriori* probability that the student will pass the course *given that he has passed the test.* You know the probabilities of the student's passing the qualifying test

given that he has passed the course and given that he has failed the course.)

(b) What is the probability that the chairman of the department is right in admitting or refusing students to the course solely on the basis of the qualifying test? (Hint: The probability he is right is the probability that a student who passes the test passes the course plus the probability that a student who fails the test fails the course.)

17. The probability of obtaining a successful result on any trial of a sequence of ten Bernoulli trials is 0.3.
   (a) What is the probability of obtaining exactly four successes?
   (b) What is the probability of obtaining at least four successes?
   (c) What is the probability of at least one success in ten trials?

18. Under the circumstances described in Exercise 17 above:
   (a) What is the probability of obtaining a success in three trials?
   (b) What is the probability that it will take at least three trials to achieve a success?

19. The probability of obtaining a failure on any trial of a sequence of Bernoulli trials is 0.7.
   (a) What is the probability that it will take exactly ten trials to achieve four successes?
   (b) What is the probability that it will take exactly eight trials to achieve four successes?
   (c) What is the probability of a failure on the first trial?

# 7/ A Final Word

The initial goal of a good many current projects in such areas of mathematical modeling as cybernetics, bionics, and general systems theory is the preparation of a conceptual framework—and a language—within which systems may be discussed, cogitated, and studied. The word *system* means such things as: a planarian ("flat worm"), a rat in a maze, a group of people in a group-therapy session, the visual apparatus (eye, optic nerve, and occipital cortex), the Freudian psychodynamic apparatus (id, libido, ego, and superego), and so on. The language of structural ("finite") mathematics that you have studied here offers certain interesting possibilities for supporting the evolution of models in these areas.

Although it may be doubted that the *entire* mathematical machinery of, say, set theory can be invoked in all its rigor, as an approach it has the obvious (and by no means slight) advantage of being both economical and conceptually convenient. As an added advantage, the language of mathematics is *manipulable* and *tractable*, whereas ordinary language often is not. Furthermore, the mathematical language lends itself more readily to translation into the terminology of computer programming than does the language of everyday conversation. The use of automated data-processing techniques is a wonderful labor-saver for the social and behavioral scientists who are often burdened by a plethora of data; it also facilitates the study of the simultaneous interaction of many more variables than could be juggled "by hand." But more than this, a computer also provides the possibility of *simulating* a system. The most obvious advantage here, of course, is the extreme rapidity with which an experiment may be run. Days, even months, of behavior may be simulated in a matter of minutes. But first one must be able to rough out some sort of mathematical model of the system that is to be simulated. And this text's primary purpose is to supply the tools for doing this—tools, moreover, which the literature indicates others are finding useful.

From another standpoint, some of the topics in this text have been chosen because they are felt to be ideally suited for illustrating the nature of mathematics and of mathematical reasoning—much more so, say, than the usual drill approach to first-year calculus. Furthermore, and most importantly perhaps, the mathematics that you have learned here is currently making its appearance in the standard sociological and psychological literature. Finally, a knowledge of these topics will stand you in good stead should you decide to continue with your mathematical studies.

As regards the literature, a number of fine papers that develop mathematical models (and that you may have skipped reading heretofore) have appeared in such standard sources as *Psychological Review*, *Psychological Bulletin*, *Sociometry*, *Econometrica*, and *Management Science*. In addition, some periodicals specialize in the publication of mathematically oriented papers in biology, psychology, and sociology, such as *Behavioral Science*, the *Bulletin of Mathematical Biophysics*, and *General Systems* (the Yearbook of the Society for General Systems Research). You may also wish to consult the book edited by Luce *et al.*,* which contains a fine selection of papers that have recently appeared in the literature dealing with mathematical models. This will familiarize you with the pioneers in this area so that you may more readily search out their work in the most recent (and future) literature.

* R. D. Luce, R. R. Bush and E. Galanter, eds., *Readings in Mathematical Psychology*, 2 vols. (New York: John Wiley & Sons, Inc., 1963).

# References for Additional Reading

1. Ashby, W. Ross, *An Introduction to Cybernetics*. New York: John Wiley & Sons, Inc., 1958.
2. Berge, C., *Theorie des Graphes et ses Applications*. Paris: Dunod, 1958.
3. Bernays, P., and A. A. Fraenkel, *Axiomatic Set Theory*. Amsterdam: North-Holland Publishing Co., 1958.
4. Birkhoff, G., and S. MacLane, *A Survey of Modern Algebra*. New York: The Macmillan Company, 1949.
5. Feller, W., *An Introduction to Probability Theory*, 2nd ed. (Vol. 1). New York: John Wiley & Sons, Inc., 1957.
6. Fraenkel, A. A., *Abstract Set Theory*. Amsterdam: North-Holland Publishing Co., 1961.
7. Fraenkel, A. A., and Y. Bar-Hillel, *Foundations of Set Theory*. Amsterdam: North-Holland Publishing Co., 1958.
8. Hall, D. W., and G. L. Spencer II, *Elementary Topology*. New York: John Wiley & Sons, Inc., 1955.
9. Harary, F., *Introduction to Digraph Theory*. To be published by Addison-Wesley.
10. Kershner, R. B., and L. R. Wilcox, *The Anatomy of Mathematics*. New York: The Ronald Press Company, 1950.
11. Rashevsky, N., *Mathematical Biophysics*, 3rd rev. ed. (2 vols). New York: Dover Publications, Inc., 1960.
12. Suppes, P., *Axiomatic Set Theory*. Princeton, N.J.: D. Van Nostrand Co., Inc., 1960.
13. Wilder, R. L., *Introduction to the Foundations of Mathematics*. New York: John Wiley & Sons, Inc., 1956.

# Answers to Exercises

## Chapter 1

1. {HHH, HHT, HTH, HTT, THH, THT, TTH, TTT}.

2. (a) {HTT, THT, TTH, TTT}.
   (b) {HHH}.
   (c) {HHH, HHT, THH}.
   (d) {HHH}.
   (e) {HHH, HHT, HTH, HTT, THH, THT, TTH}.
   (f) {HHT, HTH, THH}.
   (g) {HHT, THH}.
   (h) &. 
   (i) {TTT}. (Since the coin is tossed exactly three times, the only way at most two heads and three tails can result is as given. "At most" does not preclude the possibility of there being "none.")
   (j) &.

3. (a) $\{x \mid x$ is an odd positive integer$\}$.
   (b) $\{1, 2, 3, 5, 7, 11, 13, 17, \ldots\}$.
   (c) $\{2, 4, 6, 8, 10, 12, \ldots\}$.
   (d) $\{1, 3, 5, 7, 11, 13, 17, \ldots\}$.
   (e) $\{2\}$.
   (f) $\{3, 6, 9, 12, 15, 18, 21, \ldots\}$.
   (g) $\{x \mid x$ is a positive integer divisible by 5$\}$.
   (h) This cannot be done uniquely. Thus, the given set may be described as: $\{x \mid x$ is a positive integer divisible by 2$\}$ or $\{x \mid x$ is a positive integer divisible by 3$\}$ or $\{x \mid x$ is a positive integer divisible by 6$\}$.
   (i) Same answer as to Exercise 1 above.

4. (a) False.
   (b) False. (Notice that the set is a collection of *states*.)

    (c) False. (Here the set is a collection of cities, and Hawaii is not a city.)

    (d) False. (The null set contains no elements; in particular it doesn't contain 0.)

    (e) Neither. (The set is not well-defined, so we cannot say that $\frac{1}{2}$ belongs to it.)

    (f) False. ($\frac{1}{2}$ is an element of this set, but the *set* $\{\frac{1}{2}, \frac{1}{3}\}$ is not.)

5. (a) $2 \notin \{x \mid x$ is an odd number$\}$.

    (b) For all $x$, $x \notin \mathfrak{E}$.

    (c) $\{x \mid x$ is a unicorn$\} = \mathfrak{E}$.

    (d) $\{1, 2\} \in \{\{1, 2\}, \{2, 3\}, \{3, 4\}\}$.

    (e) $\{\{\frac{1}{1}, \frac{1}{2}\}, \{\frac{1}{2}, \frac{1}{3}\}, \{\frac{1}{3}, \frac{1}{4}\}, \ldots, \{1/n, 1/(n+1)\}\} = C$.

    (f) $\{\frac{1}{25}, \frac{1}{26}\} \in \{\{\frac{1}{1}, \frac{1}{2}\}, \ldots, \{1/n, 1/(n+1)\}\}$ or $\{\frac{1}{25}, \frac{1}{26}\} \in C$.

    (g) $\{\frac{1}{25}, \frac{1}{27}\} \notin \{\{\frac{1}{1}, \frac{1}{2}\}, \ldots, \{1/n, 1/(n+1)\}\}$ or $\{\frac{1}{25}, \frac{1}{27}\} \notin C$.

6. This question is discussed again in Chapter 2. The admission of such sets can lead to paradoxical results. One way out is to regard the set $\mathfrak{A}$ formed by including $A$ in $A$ to be a set of a higher "type." See, for example, the discussion in Chapter 3, Section 2, and Chapter 9, Section 5.2, of Reference 13.

7. The set exists but the elements do not.

## Chapter 2

1. $\{HH, HT, TH, TT\}$.

    $\{HT, HH, TH\}\{HT, HH, TT\}\{HH, TH, TT\}\{HT, TT, TH\}$.

    $\{HT, HH\}\{HT, TH\}\{HT, TT\}\{HH, TH\}\{HH, TT\}\{TH, TT\}$.

    $\{HH\}\{HT\}\{TH\}\{TT\}$.

    $\mathfrak{E}$.

2. (a) True. (Any element—be it a rock, tree or person—that is in, or belongs to, Los Angeles certainly also is in or belongs to the United States of America—contrast with answer to Exercise 4(b) of Chapter 1.)

    (b) False. (Los Angeles is not a state.)

    (c) True. (d) True. (e) True. (f) False. (g) True. (h) True. (i) True.

3. $C(5, 3) = \dfrac{5!}{3! \, (5-3)!} = \dfrac{1 \times 2 \times 3 \times 4 \times 5}{1 \times 2 \times 3 \times 1 \times 2} = \dfrac{4 \times 5}{1 \times 2} = 10$.

4. The first space may obviously be filled in any one of five different ways (that is, with any one of the five letters: $a$, $b$, $c$, $d$, or $e$); then for the next space we will only have four choices remaining, and so on. Altogether, then, there are $5 \cdot 4 \cdot 3 \cdot 2 \cdot 1 = 5!$ ways of arranging five letters (or any other five distinct things). And there will be $n!$ ways of arranging $n$ distinct objects. Each such arrangement is called a *permutation*. There are, thus, 5! permutations on 5 objects, and $n!$ permutations on $n$ things.

5. As before, the first space can be filled in any one of five different ways; then there are four choices remaining for the second space and three choices left for the last space—altogether $5 \cdot 4 \cdot 3 = 60$ permutations on five letters taken three at a time.

6. The *first* place can be filled by any one of the $n$ things, the *second* by any one of the remaining $n - 1$ things, the *third* by any one of the remaining $n - 2$ things, $\ldots$, the $m$th by any one of the remaining $n - (m - 1)$

things. Thus, the formula is $n(n - 1)(n - 2) \cdots (n - m + 1)$. This formula gives the permutations on $n$ different things taken $m$ at a time, commonly symbolized $P(n, m)$. Thus

$$P(n, m) = n(n - 1)(n - 2) \cdots (n - m + 1).$$

Notice that

$$P(n, n) = n(n - 1)(n - 2) \cdots 3 \cdot 2 \cdot 1 = n!$$

as it should.

7. $\{a, b, c\}, \{a, b, d\}, \{a, c, d\}, \{b, c, d\}$. The letters in each set can be given 3! different arrangements. Thus, for example, the set $\{a, b, c\}$ yields the arrangements $abc, acb, bac, bca, cab, cba$. Since there are four sets, there are altogether $4 \cdot 3! = 4 \cdot 3 \cdot 2 \cdot 1 = 24$ different arrangements. This is the same as $4 \cdot 3 \cdot 2 = 24$, which is the number of permutations on 4 things taken 3 at a time.

8. If we symbolize the number of combinations of $n$ things taken $m$ at a time by $C(n, m)$ and the number of permutations on $n$ things taken $m$ at a time by $P(n, m)$, it should be obvious that one formula is given by

$$C(n, m)m! = P(n, m)$$

or

$$C(n, m) = \frac{P(n, m)}{m!}$$

Using the formula for $P(n, m)$ given above, we may write this as

$$C(n, m) = \frac{n(n - 1)(n - 2) \cdots (n - m + 1)}{m!}.$$

On multiplying the numerator and the denominator by $(n - m)!$, we may rewrite this as

$$C(n, m) = \frac{n(n - 1)(n - 2) \cdots (n - m + 1)(n - m)(n - m - 1) \cdots 3 \cdot 2 \cdot 1}{m! \, (n - m)!}$$

or

$$C(n, m) = \frac{n!}{m! \, (n - m)!}.$$

The reader should convince himself that

$$n(n - 1)(n - 2) \cdots (n - m + 1) \cdot (n - m)! = n!$$

with a few examples. Notice that the factorial applies only to the last parenthesis on the left side of the equals sign; the terms preceding it are not factorials.

9. (a) $P^A = \{\{a\}, \{b\}, \{a, b\}, \mathfrak{E}\}$.
   (b) No.
   (c) Yes.
   (d) Yes.

10. (a) The null set $\mathfrak{E}$ is a subset of *every* set, so, in particular, $\mathfrak{E} \subseteq \mathfrak{E}$. But, also, every set is a subset (improper) of itself, so again, $\mathfrak{E} \subseteq \mathfrak{E}$. Thus, the collection of all subsets of $\mathfrak{E}$ is simply $\{\mathfrak{E}\}$—that is, $P^{\mathfrak{E}} = \{\mathfrak{E}\}$.
    (b) The subsets of $\{\mathfrak{E}\}$ are: $\mathfrak{E}$ because $\mathfrak{E}$ is a subset of every set; and $\{\mathfrak{E}\}$, because every set is a subset of itself. Thus,

$$P P^{\mathfrak{E}} = \{\mathfrak{E}, \{\mathfrak{E}\}\} = P^{\{\mathfrak{E}\}}.$$

An interesting *sequence* of collections of subsets of a given set results in the case where the set initially chosen is empty. Let us put

$$S_0 = \{\mathfrak{E}\},$$
$$S_1 = \{\mathfrak{E}, \{\mathfrak{E}\}\},$$
$$S_2 = \{\mathfrak{E}, \{\mathfrak{E}\}, \{\{\mathfrak{E}\}, \{\mathfrak{E}, \{\mathfrak{E}\}\}\},$$

and so on. Thus, we obtain a sequence of sets: $S_1, S_2, \ldots, S_n$, where $S_{j+1}$ is the power set of $S_j$. And if $n_j$ is the number of elements of $S_j$, then $n_{j+1} = 2^{n_j}$. Furthermore, notice that $S_0 \subset S_1 \subset S_2 \subset \cdots$.

We have here an "algorithm" or routine for, given any set $S_i$, generating the "next" set $S_{i+1}$—that is, for "ordering" (see Section 4.4) the sets much as the natural numbers may be ordered by $<$ (read "less than"):

$$1 < 2 < 3 < \cdots.$$

But there is this important difference. Whereas it is nonsense to speak of a natural number between two neighboring natural numbers in the above family, you can readily find a set $S$ between $S_1$ and $S_2$ such that $S_1 \subset S \subset S_2$. Indeed, for every pair of sets $S_i$ and $S_{i+1}$ ($i \neq 0$) in the above sequence you can always find at least one set $S$ such that $S_i \subset S \subset S_{i+1}$. The situation here thus resembles that of the rational numbers (such as "fractions") wherein between any two rational numbers you can always find another. But, interestingly enough, while it makes no sense to speak of the next rational number (for example, what is the very next larger fraction after, say, $\frac{1}{4}$?), the algorithm above gives us the routine for generating the next set $S_{i+1}$ after any set $S_i$.

(c) Yes. (What is the difference? See discussion under (b) above.)

(d) and (e) $P^{\mathfrak{E}} \subset P^{\{\mathfrak{E}\}} \subset P^{\{\{\mathfrak{E}\}\}}$.

11. Since $\mathfrak{E}$ is a subset of any set, such as $A$, among the subsets of $A$, one will find $\mathfrak{E}$ listed—which is exactly what $\mathfrak{E} \in P^A$ says. By the same token, $A \subseteq A$, therefore $A$ will be listed in the collection of subsets of $A$, which is $P^A$.

12. (a) This may be shown in two parts: (i) By showing that $P^A \subseteq P^B$ implies $A \subseteq B$ and (ii) by showing that $A \subseteq B$ implies $P^A \subseteq P^B$. The first part may be reasoned as follows: Suppose $P^A \subseteq P^B$; this means that every $S \in P^A$ is an $S \in P^B$. Now, suppose $A \not\subseteq B$; this means that there exists at least one $x \in A$ such that $x \notin B$. Thus, among the subsets of $A$ there will appear at least one, namely $\{x\}$, that is not among the subsets of $B$—which contradicts the assumption that $P^A \subseteq P^B$. Therefore, it can not be that $A \not\subseteq B$; we must have $A \subseteq B$, if $P^A \subseteq P^B$. The reader may supply the remaining arguments (part (ii)) to complete the proof.

(b), (c), and (d) follow immediately from the definition of $P^A$ (you should convince yourself of this).

13. (a) $\overline{\mathfrak{E}} = \mathfrak{U}$.

(b) $\overline{\mathfrak{U}} = \mathfrak{E}$.

14. (a) False.

(b) True.

(c) True. (In fact, $\overline{\overline{\mathfrak{U}}} = \mathfrak{E}$.)

(d) True. (In fact, $\overline{\overline{\mathfrak{E}}} = \mathfrak{U}$.)

15. Suppose it were possible to have some empty set $\mathfrak{E}'$ distinct from $\mathfrak{E}$. This would be possible only if $\mathfrak{E}$ contained some element not in $\mathfrak{E}$, or vice versa. But this is ridiculous by definition of "empty set." Therefore, there cannot be some empty set $\mathfrak{E}'$ distinct from $\mathfrak{E}$, and there is only one empty set.

16. This follows at once from a result in logic that "$x$ implies $y$" is equivalent to "not-$y$ implies not-$x$", for example, "if it has been raining, then the streets are wet" is equivalent to "if the streets are not wet, then it has not been raining." Notice that this is *not* equivalent to "if it has not been raining, then the streets are not wet" (a water-truck may have just passed by).

17. The proof has two parts: (i) argue that $A = B$ implies $A \subseteq B$ and $B \subseteq A$ and (ii) that $A \subseteq B$ and $B \subseteq A$ imply $A = B$.

18. Since $\{\{a\}, \{a, b\}\} = \{\{c\}, \{c, d\}\}$, every element in the first set must be an element in the second, and vice versa. Thus, in particular, $\{c\} \in \{\{a\}, \{a, b\}\}$ so that either $\{c\} = \{a\}$ or $\{c\} = \{a, b\}$. The latter equality can only hold if $a = b$, for a set with exactly one element can obviously not be equal to a set containing two or more distinct elements. But if $a = b$, then $\{a, b\} = \{a, a\} = \{a\}$, so that in this case we have $\{c\} = \{a\}$, which gives $c = a$. Similarly, we conclude that $\{a, b\} \in \{\{c\}, \{c, d\}\}$, whence $\{a, b\} = \{c, d\}$, because in view of $a \neq b$ we can *not* have $\{a, b\} = \{c\}$—as just brought out above. Now, since we have already shown that $a = c$, we have $\{a, b\} = \{a, d\}$, so that, in view of $a \neq b$, we conclude $b = d$.

19. Yes. If $S = \{a, b\}$ then $\{a\} \subset S$ and $a \in \{a\}$.

20. Yes, for example with $S = \{a, \{a\}\}$ we have $\{a\} \in P^S$—that is, $\{a\}$ is one of the subsets of $S$, and as we see, also, $\{a\} \in S$.

# Chapter 3

1. (a) Evidently $\mathfrak{U} \cup \mathfrak{E} = \mathfrak{U}$, since $\mathfrak{E}$ is empty and we know that $\mathfrak{U} \subseteq \mathfrak{U}$; therefore, $\mathfrak{U} \subseteq \mathfrak{U} \cup \mathfrak{E}$.
   (b) By definition, $\mathfrak{U} \cup \mathfrak{E}$ is a *set* and the null set is a subset of every set; therefore, $\mathfrak{E} \subseteq \mathfrak{U} \cup \mathfrak{E}$.

2. Every element in $A$ is surely an element in $A$ or $B$, which is all that $A \subseteq A \cup B$ says. Notice that, by the same token, $B \subseteq A \cup B$. Alternatively, since $A \cup B = B \cup A$, the second result is established once the first is. The result just derived may be generalized as follows. Let $I$ be an index set and $\{A_\alpha\}$ a collection of subsets of $\mathfrak{U}$ indexed by $I$. Then

$$A_\alpha \subseteq \bigcup_{\alpha \in I} A_\alpha \quad \text{for every} \quad \alpha \in I.$$

Notice how much more this says, yet how compactly.

3. (a) $A \cup B = A$.
   (b) We must show both that $A \cup B \subseteq A$ and that $A \subseteq A \cup B$ (which evidently is equivalent to showing that $A \cup B = A$). We have already shown that $A \subseteq A \cup B$ in Exercise 2 above. It remains only to show that $A \cup B \subseteq A$. If $B \subseteq A$ (as assumed in the hypothesis), then every element in $B$ is also an element in $A$ by definition of $\subseteq$. And every element in $A$ is obviously an element in $A$, so that every element in $A$ or $B$ is an element in $A$, which is just what $A \cup B \subseteq A$ says.

4. Suppose that $B \nsubseteq A$; then there must be at least one element in $B$ that is not in $A$, and this element is surely in $A \cup B$. But this means that there is an element in $A \cup B$ that is not in $A$, contradicting the hypothesis that $A \cup B = A$. Therefore, the hypothesis implies that $B \subseteq A$.

5. (a) From Exercise 2 above, $A \subseteq A \cup \mathfrak{E}$. Now, suppose $x \in A \cup \mathfrak{E}$; then, evidently, $x \in A$ (since $\mathfrak{E}$ itself is empty); thus, $A \cup \mathfrak{E} \subseteq A$. From these two results we conclude that $\mathfrak{E} \cup A = A$. (Recall that $A \subseteq B$ and $B \subseteq A$ imply $A = B$.)

   (b) Again, from Exercise 2 above, $\mathfrak{U} \subseteq A \cup \mathfrak{U}$. And since every set is a subset of the universal set, we have $A \cup \mathfrak{U} \subseteq \mathfrak{U}$. Therefore, $A \cup \mathfrak{U} = \mathfrak{U}$.

   (c) Once more, by Exercise 2 above, $A \subseteq A \cup A$. Furthermore, if $x \in A \cup A$, then $x \in A$ or $x \in A$—that is, $x \in A$; therefore $A \cup A \subseteq A$. So $A \cup A = A$.

6. $\bigcup\limits_{X \in \mathfrak{A}} X$ is the set of all those (and only those) elements which belong to *at least* one set of the family $\mathfrak{A}$.

7. (a) Yes; this follows immediately from the definitions of $\cup$ and $\subseteq$.

   (b) No; but every set *is* the union of all of its one-element subsets.

8. (a) If $x \in A \cap B$, then, by definition of $\cap$, $x \in A$ (and $x \in B$, of course, but we don't need that fact here); therefore, by definition of $\subseteq$, $A \cap B \subseteq A$.

   (b) If $x \in A \cap B$, then, by definition of $\cap$, $x \in B$; therefore, $A \cap B \subseteq B$. Again, we may generalize as follows. Let $I$ be an index set and $\{A_\alpha\}$ a collection of subsets of $\mathfrak{U}$ indexed by $I$. Then

$$\bigcap_{\alpha \in I} A_\alpha \subseteq A_\alpha \qquad \text{for every} \quad \alpha \in I.$$

9. (a) By the previous results, $A \cap A \subseteq A$. Now, if $x \in A$, then, obviously, $x \in A \cap A$; therefore, $A \subseteq A \cap A$. So $A \cap A = A$.

   (b) Again, by the previous result, $A \cap \mathfrak{E} \subseteq \mathfrak{E}$. But, also, $\mathfrak{E} \subseteq (A \cap \mathfrak{E})$—since $\mathfrak{E}$ is a subset of every set. Therefore, $A \cap \mathfrak{E} = \mathfrak{E}$. One might also argue that since $\mathfrak{E}$ is empty, the set of elements that are simultaneously in $\mathfrak{E}$ and $A$ is null; therefore, $A \cap \mathfrak{E}$ is null—that is, $A \cap \mathfrak{E} = \mathfrak{E}$. But this is not quite as satisfactory as the straightforward proof above, since it sneaks in the intuitive and imprecise notion of "emptiness."

   (c) Once again, $A \cap \mathfrak{U} \subseteq A$. Now, let $x$ be any element in $A$; then, since $\mathfrak{U}$ is the universal set, $x$ also belongs to $\mathfrak{U}$. To say that $x \in A$ and $x \in \mathfrak{U}$ is, by definition (of intersection), to say that $x \in \mathfrak{U} \cap A$. We have shown that $x \in A$ implies $x \in A \cap \mathfrak{U}$—that is, $A \subseteq A \cap \mathfrak{U}$. Thus, since $A \cap \mathfrak{U} \subseteq A$ and $A \subseteq A \cap \mathfrak{U}$, we conclude that $A \cap \mathfrak{U} = A$.

10. Since, as we have shown, $A \cap B \subseteq A$ and $A \subseteq (A \cup B)$, we conclude that $A \cap B \subseteq A \cup B$. (Recall that $\subseteq$ is transitive; that is, $A \subseteq B$ and $B \subseteq C$ imply that $A \subseteq C$.)

11. (a) $A \cup B$.

   (b) $A \cap B$.

   (c) The answer otherwise would be "the empty set."

12. (a) We have already shown (in Exercise 8) that $A \cap B \subseteq A$; it remains only to show that $A \subseteq A \cap B$ here. Since $A \subseteq B$, every element in $A$ is an element in $B$; therefore, every element in $A$ is an element in $A$ and $B$ (since every element in $A$ is automatically an element in $A$); thus $A \subseteq A \cap B$.

   (b) Suppose $A \nsubseteq B$. Then there must be at least one element in $A$ that is not in $B$. This element surely is not in $A \cap B$ (since this set consists only of those elements that are in *both* $A$ and $B$). Thus, there is an element in $A$ that is not in $A \cap B$, which means, of course, that $A \neq A \cap B$. But we are given (by hypothesis) that $A \cap B = A$. Thus, it cannot be that $A \nsubseteq B$.

13. Let $x \in (A - B)$. Then, by definition, $x \in A$ and $x \notin B$. In particular, $x \in A$—that is, if $x \in (A - B)$, then $x \in A$. Therefore, $(A - B) \subseteq A$.

14. Since $A \subseteq B$, *every* $x \in A$ is an $x \in B$. Thus, there are no $x \in A$ that are not in $B$—that is, $A - B = \mathfrak{E}$.

15. Suppose $x \in (A - B) \cap B$. Then, by definition (of $\cap$), $x \in A - B$ and $x \in B$. But the former fact (by definition of "difference") means that $x \in A$ and $x \notin B$. Since there can be no element satisfying both $x \in B$ and $x \notin B$, therefore, $(A - B) \cap B = \mathfrak{E}$.

16. This is one way of defining the things called natural numbers, and symbolized $1, 2, 3, \ldots$, in terms of the more fundamental notions of set theory. $0$ may be identified with $\mathfrak{E}$. Notice that this process will generate *all* the names $1, 2, 3, \ldots$ and there is never a set between two successive (adjacent) sets in the family.

17. (a) $A \cup A = A$; therefore, $(A \cup A) - A$ is the same as $A - A$, which, evidently, is equal to $\mathfrak{E}$.

   (b) $A - A = \mathfrak{E}$; therefore $A \cup (A - A) = A \cup \mathfrak{E} = A$.

18. $B - \bar{A}$ is the set of all elements that are in $B$ and not in $\bar{A}$—that is, in $A$. But this is the set of all elements in $B$ and $A$—that is, in $A \cap B$.

19. Suppose $x \in (B - A)$; then $x \in B$ and $x \notin A$—that is, $x \in \bar{A}$. Thus, $x \in (B - A)$ implies that $x \in \bar{A}$, whence $(B - A) \subseteq \bar{A}$.

20. Suppose $x \in A$. Since $A \cap B = \mathfrak{E}$, $x \notin B$—that is, $x \in \bar{B}$. Thus $x \in A$ implies $x \in \bar{B}$—that is, $A \subseteq \bar{B}$.

21. $A \vartriangle B = A \cup \bar{A} \cap A \cup B \cap \bar{B} \cup \bar{A} \cap \bar{B} \cup B$

   $\qquad = \mathfrak{U} \cap A \cup B \cap \bar{A} \cup \bar{B} \cap \mathfrak{U}$

   $\qquad = A \cup B \cap \bar{A} \cup \bar{B}$

   $\qquad = A \cup B \cap \overline{A \cap B} = (A \cup B) - (A \cap B).$

22. (a) $\overline{T + J} = \bar{T} \cdot \bar{J}$.

   (b) $\overline{D \cdot \bar{P}} = \bar{D} + P$.

   (c) $\overline{D + \bar{F}} = \bar{D} \cdot F$.

   (d) $C \cdot (\bar{C} + D) = C \cdot \bar{C} + C \cdot D = C \cdot D$.

   (e) $(S + L) \cdot \overline{S \cdot L} = (S + L) \cdot (\bar{S} + \bar{L}) = S \cdot \bar{S} + S \cdot \bar{L} + L \cdot \bar{S} + L \cdot \bar{L}$

   $\qquad = S \cdot \bar{L} + L \cdot \bar{S}.$

23. The premises are

$$\bar{S} + R + B = 1, \qquad \bar{R} \cdot \bar{B} = 1.$$

The second expression may be rewritten as

$$\overline{R + B} = 1$$

whence

$$R + B = 0,$$

whereupon, substituting in the first expression,

$$\bar{S} + 0 = 1,$$

whence

$$\bar{S} = 1$$

or

$$S = 0.$$

(The first conclusion asserts the statement: "These results are not significant"; the second form of the conclusion, which amounts to the same thing, *denies* the statement: "These results are significant.")

24.  The premises are

$$S + \overline{W} + I = 1,$$

$$W \cdot \bar{I} + \overline{C} = 1,$$

$$C = 1.$$

The last premise may be written, equivalently, as

$$\overline{C} = 0,$$

and substituting in the previous gives

$$W \cdot \bar{I} + 0 = 1$$

or

$$W \cdot \bar{I} = 1.$$

Therefore

$$\overline{W \cdot \bar{I}} = 0,$$

whence

$$\overline{W} + I = 0.$$

Substituting this result in the first premise yields

$$S = 1$$

—the conclusion.

25.  (i) $\overline{P_1 \cdot P_2} + L = 1.$

(ii) $\bar{L} + M = 1.$

(iii) $B \cdot \overline{M} = 1.$

(iv) $P_1 = 1.$

The only way for (iii) to hold is for $B$ and $\overline{M}$ to be equal to 1—in particular, $\overline{M} = 1$; therefore, $M = 0$, which, substituting in (ii), results in $\bar{L} = 1$ or $L = 0$. This result, substituted in (i), gives $\overline{P_1 \cdot P_2} = 1$ or $\bar{P}_1 + \bar{P}_2 = 1$. But, from (iv), we have $\bar{P}_. = 0\cdot$ therefore, $\bar{P}_2 = 1$—the conclusion.

26. The policy is valid only if

$$\overline{(T + M + N \cdot \overline{T})} + (T \cdot \overline{M} + N).$$

There are several ways to proceed from here in simplifying this expression—obviously we cannot list them all; but the point is one can proceed in a more or less arbitrary mechanical fashion. Here is a sample procedure. In practice, a number of the separate intermediate steps we have included would be done simultaneously, as a single step.

$$\overline{\overline{(T + M + N \cdot \overline{T})} + (T \cdot \overline{M} + N)} = (T + M + N \cdot \overline{T}) \cdot \overline{(T \cdot \overline{M} + N)}.$$

Then

$$(T + M + N \cdot \overline{T}) \cdot \overline{(T \cdot \overline{M} + N)} = (T + M + N \cdot \overline{T}) \cdot (\overline{T \cdot \overline{M}} \cdot \overline{N})$$

and

$$(T + M + N \cdot \overline{T}) \cdot (\overline{T \cdot \overline{M}} \cdot \overline{N}) = (T + M + N \cdot \overline{T}) \cdot (\overline{T} + M \cdot \overline{N}).$$

From here on we will just continue simplifying the right sides and combine several steps at once.

$$\begin{aligned}(T + M + N \cdot \overline{T}) \cdot (\overline{T} \cdot M \cdot \overline{N}) &= T \cdot \overline{T} + \overline{T} \cdot M + \overline{T} \cdot N \\ &\quad + T \cdot M \cdot \overline{N} + M \cdot \overline{N} + N \cdot \overline{T} \cdot M \cdot \overline{N} \\ &= 0 + \overline{T} \cdot M + N \cdot \overline{T} + T \cdot M \cdot \overline{N} + M \cdot \overline{N} + 0 \\ &= \overline{T} \cdot (M + N) + \overline{N} \cdot M\end{aligned}$$

Thus, the insurance policy is valid only if the insured is not over 21 and married or in a nonhazardous occupation, or if he is in a hazardous occupation and married.

27. (a)
$$\begin{aligned}(A \cap B) \cap (A \cap C) &= (A \cap B \cap A) \cap C \\ &= (A \cap B) \cap C = A \cap (B \cap C).\end{aligned}$$

    (b) is proved similarly.

28. (a) No.
    (b) No.
    (c) Yes.

29. (a) This simply says that if $x \in A$ implies $x \in C$ and $x \in B$ implies $x \in C$, then $(x \in A$ or $x \in B)$ implies $x \in C$, which is surely true.
    (b) follows similarly.

30. We have to show that $A \subseteq B$ implies $A \cup B = B$ and, conversely, $A \cup B = B$ implies $A \subseteq B$. Suppose $A \subseteq B$. We know that, always, $B \subseteq B$. These two facts combine with the result of Exercise 29(a) to yield $A \cup B \subseteq B$. We also know, from a previous result, that $B \subseteq A \cup B$. Therefore, $A \cup B = B$. Conversely, if $A \cup B = B$, then $A \subseteq B$ (because $A \subseteq A \cup B$, as was shown in Exercise 2).

31.
$$\begin{aligned}X = X \cap \mathfrak{U} &= X \cap \overline{A \cup \overline{A}} \\ &= X \cap A \cup X \cap \overline{A}\end{aligned}$$

Therefore $X \cap \mathfrak{U} = X \cap \overline{A}$ (since it is given that $X \cap A = \mathfrak{E}$); this is to say that $X = X \cap \overline{A}$. Now, $\overline{A} \cap A \cup X = \overline{A} \cap \mathfrak{U}$ (since it is given that $A \cup X = \mathfrak{U}$). The left side expands to yield: $A \cap \overline{A} \cup \overline{A} \cap X = \overline{A} \cap \mathfrak{U}$. Therefore, $\overline{A} \cap X = \overline{A} \cap \mathfrak{U} = \overline{A}$. From $\overline{A} \cap X = \overline{A}$ and $\overline{A} \cap X = X$ we conclude that $X = \overline{A}$.

32. Suppose $A \subseteq \mathfrak{U}$ has two complements, $A_1$ and $A_2$. Then, from the properties of complements,

$$\mathfrak{E} = A \cap A_1 = A \cap A_2$$

and

$$\mathfrak{U} = A \cup A_1 = A \cup A_2.$$

Now,

$$A_1 = A_1 \cap (A \cup A_2) = (A_1 \cap A) \cup (A_1 \cap A_2),$$

since $A \cup A_2 = \mathfrak{U}$ and $A_1 \cap \mathfrak{U} = A_1$ (because $X \cap \mathfrak{U} = X$ for *any* set $X$)—the end result was obtained using the distributive law (item 6, Section 3.6). Now, since $A_1 \cap A = A_2 \cap A$, we may write the above result as

$$A_1 = (A_2 \cap A) \cup (A_1 \cap A_2) = A_2 \cap (A_1 \cup A),$$

the end result following by the distributive law again (this time read from right to left—see item 6, Section 3.6). But $A_1 \cup A = \mathfrak{U}$; therefore

$$A_1 = A_2 \cap \mathfrak{U} = A_2.$$

33. $\{x \mid -2 \leqslant x < 4\}$.

34. $\{x \mid -4 < x < 2\}$.

35. Except those in $\{x \mid -4 \leqslant x \leqslant 2\}$. Thus, if we let $A = \{x \mid -4 \leqslant x \leqslant 2\}$, then

$$\{x \mid x > 2\} \cup \{x \mid x < -4\} = \{x \mid x \in \bar{A}\}.$$

36. (a) $(A \cup B) \cap (\bar{A} \cap \bar{B}) = [(A \cup B) \cap \bar{A}] \cup [(A \cup B) \cap \bar{B}]$

$$= (A \cap \bar{A}) \cup (B \cap \bar{A}) \cup (A \cap \bar{B}) \cup (B \cap \bar{B})$$

$$= (B \cap \bar{A}) \cup (A \cap \bar{B}) = (B - A) \cup (A - B)$$

$$= A \triangle B.$$

(b) $(A \cup B) - (A \cap B) = (A \cup B) \cap (\overline{A \cap B}) = (A \cup B) \cap (\bar{A} \cup \bar{B}) = A \triangle B$, as has just been shown above. (The next-to-the-last result is obtained using De Morgan's law, item 14, Section 3.6.)

37. (a) $A = A + 0$        by P-4

    $= A + A \cdot \bar{A}$        by P-11

    $= (A + A) \cdot (A + \bar{A})$        by P-3 (second part)

    $= (A + A) \cdot 1$        by P-10

    $= A + A$        by P-7.

(b) $A = A \cdot 1$        by P-7

    $= A \cdot (A + \bar{A})$        by P-10

    $= A \cdot A + A \cdot \bar{A}$        by P-3

    $= A \cdot A + 0$        by P-11

    $= A \cdot A$        by P-4.

(c) $1 = A + \bar{A}$        by P-10,

    $A + 1 = A + 1$        a property of equality

    $= A + (A + \bar{A})$        substituting $A + \bar{A}$ for 1 (from above)

    $= (A + A) + \bar{A}$        by P-2 (second part)

    $= A + \bar{A}$        by P-8 (proved in (a) above)

    $= 1$        by P-10.

**38.**  $\bar{1} = \bar{1} \cdot 1$    by P-7 (here $\bar{1}$ is $A$)

$\quad\ = 1 \cdot \bar{1}$    by P-1 (first part)

$\quad\ = 0$    by P-11.

Similarly,

$\bar{0} = \bar{0} + 0$    by P-4

$\quad\ = 0 + \bar{0}$    by P-2 (first part)

$\quad\ = 1$    by P-10.

## Chapter 4

1.  $\{(1, (a, u)), (1, (a, v)), (1, (b, u)), (1, (b, v)), (2, (a, u)), \ldots, (3, (b, v))\}$.
    Note that the answer consists of a collection of ordered pairs, each of whose
    second element is itself an ordered pair. Obviously, $(A \times B) \times C$ would
    consist of a collection of ordered pairs whose *first* elements are themselves
    ordered pairs, and so, $A \times (B \times C) \neq (A \times B) \times C$—that is, the oper-
    ation is, in general, not associative. A simple scheme for enumerating the
    elements of the set of ordered *triplets*, $A \times B \times C$, is shown below:

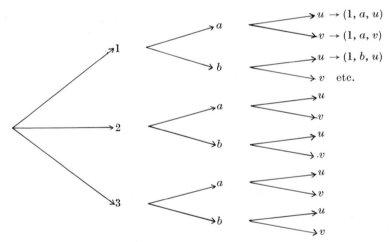

2.  (a)  We have to show that $A \times (B \cup C) \subseteq (A \times B) \cup (A \times C)$ and vice
        versa. Let $(x, y)$ be an element of $A \times (B \cup C)$; then $x \in A$ and
        $y \in B \cup C$, so that $y$ belongs to $B$ or $C$ (possibly both). If $y \in B$ then,
        remembering that $x \in A$, $(x, y) \in A \times B$ and surely $(x, y) \in (A \times B) \cup$
        $(A \times C)$. This result still holds, of course, if $y$ happens to belong to
        both $B$ and $C$. Thus, in any event, if $(x, y) \in A \times (B \cup C)$ then
        $(x, y) \in (A \times B) \cup (A \times C)$; therefore, $A \times (B \cup C) \subseteq (A \times B) \cup$
        $(A \times C)$. The reader may complete the proof by showing that
        $(A \times B) \cup (A \times C) \subseteq A \times (B \cup C)$—be sure to consider all possi-
        bilities.
    (b)  We have to show that $A \times (B \cap C) \subseteq (A \times B) \cap (A \times C)$ and vice
        versa. We prove the latter and leave the former to the reader. Suppose

$(x, y) \in (A \times B) \cap (A \times C)$; then $(x, y) \in A \times B$ and $(x, y) \in A \times C$; so $x \in A$, $y \in B$ and $y \in C$—that is, $y \in B \cap C$. Thus, $(x, y) \in A \times (B \cap C)$ and therefore $(A \times B) \cap (A \times C) \subseteq A \times (B \cap C)$.

3.

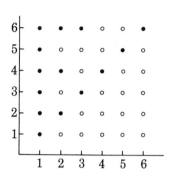

Domain $= \{1, 2, 3, 4, 5, 6\}$
Range $= \{1, 2, 3, 4, 5, 6\}$

4.

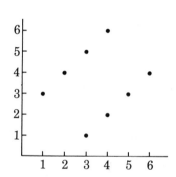

Domain $= \{1, 2, 3, 4, 5, 6\}$
Range $= \{1, 2, 3, 4, 5, 6\}$

5.

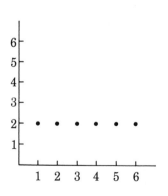

Domain $= \{1, 2, 3, 4, 5, 6\}$
Range $= \{2\}$

Domain $= \{3\}$
Range $= \{1, 2, 3, 4, 5, 6\}$

6.  (a)  $R$ is not transitive because although we have $(1, 2) \in R$ and $(2, 3) \in R$ we do *not* have $(1, 3) \in R$.
    (b)  $R$ is reflexive because we have $(1, 1) \in R$ (that is, $1\ R\ 1$) and $(2, 2) \in R$ and $(3, 3) \in R$—that is, every element in $R$ is related to itself.
    (c)  $R$ is not symmetric because while we have $(1, 2) \in R$ we do not have $(2, 1) \in R$.

7.  Yes. Examples abound–e.g., blames himself.

8.  Examples abound:  set inclusion, less-than-or-equal-to, at-least-as-old-as.

9.  Yes. Example: is-greater-than.

10. Yes. Example: is-a-first-cousin-of.

11. Yes. Example: is-a-nephew-of.

12. Yes. Example: is-at-most-a-mile-from.

13. Since it is given that $(a, b) \in R$, we can conclude that $a\ R\ b$, and then, by symmetry, that $b\ R\ a$. Using transitivity on $a\ R\ b$ and $b\ R\ a$, we conclude $a\ R\ a$. Using transitivity on $b\ R\ a$ and $a\ R\ b$, we conclude $b\ R\ b$. Therefore, $R$ is reflexive. However, this does not prove, in general, that symmetry and transitivity imply reflexivity, for suppose there is no $b$ in the first place such that $a\ R\ b$. This may be a subtle point to some readers and may be overlooked. But the fact that the properties of symmetry, reflexivity, and transitivity are independent (no two imply the third) is the important thing to remember.

14. (a)  $\{2, 5, 8, 11, 14, 17, 20, \ldots\} = S_2$.
    (b)  $\{0, 3, 6, 9, 12, 15, 18, 21, \ldots\} = S_0$.
    (c)  $\{1, 4, 7, 10, 13, 16, 19, \ldots\} = S_1$.
    (d)  These three equivalence classes do form a partition of the set $P = \{1, 2, 3, 4, 5, 6, \ldots\}$ of all positive integers, and

    $$S_1 \cup S_2 \cup S_3 = P$$

    while

    $$S_1 \cap S_2 \cap S_3 = \mathfrak{E}.$$

15. 

16. 

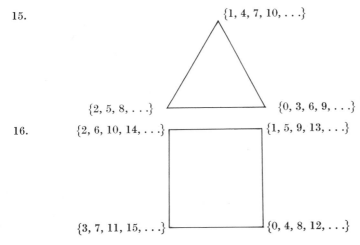

17.

| + | ∅ | I | II | III |
|---|---|---|----|-----|
| ∅ | ∅ | I | II | III |
| I | I | II | III | ∅ |
| II | II | III | ∅ | I |
| III | III | ∅ | I | II |

| · | ∅ | I | II | III |
|---|---|---|----|-----|
| ∅ | ∅ | ∅ | ∅ | ∅ |
| I | ∅ | I | II | III |
| II | ∅ | II | ∅ | II |
| III | ∅ | III | II | I |

The fact that II + III = I, for example, should cause no more consternation than the fact that, say, $7 + 7 = 2$ *on a clock!*

The identity under ( + ) is ∅ and under ( · ) is I. Also, every element has an inverse under ( + ) but not under ( · ). Thus, for example, while III and I are self-inverse under ( · ), since

$$\text{III} \cdot \text{III} = \text{I}$$

$$\text{and } \text{I} \cdot \text{I} = \text{I},$$

I does not appear anywhere in the third row in the body of the table, so II has no inverse. Notice, for example, that II is its own inverse under +, since II + II = ∅.

18. $(a, b)\,R\,(a, b)$ because, evidently, $ab = ba$; therefore, $R$ is reflexive. Suppose $(a, b)\,R\,(c, d)$, then $ad = bc$, which implies $cb = da$, and so $(c, d)\,R\,(a, b)$, whence $R$ is symmetric. Suppose $(a, b)\,R\,(c, d)$ and $(c, d)\,R\,(e, f)$, then $ad = bc$ and $cf = de$, so $(ad)(cf) = (bc)(de)$ or $af = be$; that is, $(a, b)\,R\,(e, f)$ and $R$ is transitive. Notice that if we define $(a, b) = a/b$, then, for example, $(2, 4)\,R\,(1, 2)$ means that $\frac{2}{4}$ is equivalent to $\frac{1}{2}$.

19. Proof is similar to that above.

20. $R$ is obviously symmetric from the way it is defined and the fact that there is no difference between ($x\,Q\,y$ and $y\,Q\,x$) and ($y\,Q\,x$ and $x\,Q\,y$). Since $Q$ is reflexive, we have $x\,Q\,x$, and therefore ($x\,Q\,x$ and $x\,Q\,x$) holds for all $x$, whence $x\,R\,x$ for all $x$. Finally, if $x\,R\,y$ and $y\,R\,z$ hold, then ($x\,Q\,y$ and $y\,Q\,x$) and ($y\,Q\,z$ and $z\,Q\,y$) hold. But since $Q$ is transitive, we can use these facts to conclude from $x\,Q\,y$ and $y\,Q\,z$ that $x\,Q\,z$. Similarly, $z\,Q\,x$ from the remaining two cases. Therefore, from $x\,Q\,z$ and $z\,Q\,x$ we conclude $x\,R\,z$, so $R$ is transitive.

21. This follows immediately from the fact that an equivalence relation is reflexive and transitive. The fact that it also happens to be symmetric doesn't affect matters one way or another.

22. Suppose $x\,R\,y$ and $y\,R\,z$, then we have $x\,Q\,y$ and not-($y\,Q\,x$) and $y\,Q\,z$ and not-($z\,Q\,y$). From the first and third fact we conclude (since $Q$ is transitive) that $x\,Q\,z$. Suppose we also had $z\,Q\,x$; this together with $x\,Q\,y$ would imply $z\,Q\,y$ (since $Q$ is transitive). But this contradicts the fact of not-($z\,Q\,y$). Hence we must have, instead, not-($z\,Q\,y$), in which case $x\,R\,z$ and $R$ is transitive. The fact that $R$ is asymmetric almost falls right out of the definition. If we had both $x\,R\,y$ and $y\,R\,x$, this would mean $x\,Q\,y$ and not-($y\,Q\,x$) and $y\,Q\,x$ and not-($x\,Q\,y$)—clearly an inconsistent set of statements.

23. Consider any element $s_1 \in S$. If there is no $s_2 \in S$ such that $s_2\,P\,s_1$, then $s_1$ is maximal. Otherwise, choose an $s_2$ and repeat the process. How do we know that we will get a new $s_i$ each time? Because all the elements of $S$ are distinct ("different")—recall the definition of a set. How do we know

that this repeating process won't bring us back to our starting point—that is, how do we know that we won't get a series like $s_1 P s_2$, $s_2 P s_3$, $s_3 P s_4$, ..., $s_{n-1} P s_n$, $s_n P s_1$? Because $P$ is transitive and so $s_1 P s_2$ and $s_2 P s_3$ imply $s_1 P s_3$; then $s_1 P s_3$ and $s_3 P s_4$ imply $s_1 P s_4$; and so on, until finally we derive the result $s_1 P s_n$. But then we cannot also have $s_n P s_1$, because $P$ is asymmetric. So we conclude that the process of repetition above will give a new $s_i$ at each step. And since $S$ is finite, we must eventually come to an $s_i$ that is maximal. The proof of the existence of a minimal element is similar. You are encouraged to go through the reasoning step by step.

24. You will recall that if $a R b$ and $R'$ is the converse of $R$, then $b R' a$. Now since $R$ is a weak ordering, we have $a R b$ and $b R c$ imply $a R c$. The converses of $a R b$, $b R c$, and $a R c$ are $b R' a$, $c R' b$, and $c R' a$. So we have that $c R' b$ and $b R' a$ and $c R' a$ all hold, showing that $R'$ is transitive. $R'$ is obviously reflexive, for the converse of $a R a$ is $a R' a$.

25. You must show that if $P'$ is the converse of $P$, then $P'$ is also transitive and irreflexive (or asymmetric, since an asymmetric relation is automatically irreflexive).

26. (a) Yes. (b) No, because there are "incomparable" elements (for example, 4 is not a multiple of 5). (c) Yes. (d) No. ($R$ is not even symmetric.) (e) No, because there are incomparable elements.

27. (a) Yes. (b) No. (c) Yes. (d) No. (e) No.

28. The accompanying diagram shows that 4 and 6 are each multiples of 2; that, in addition, 6 is a multiple of 3; and so on. Notice that there is exactly one minimal element; it, therefore, is the minimum. That is to say, there is no $y \in S$ such that $1 M y$ and 1 is the only number for which this is true. There are no maximal elements. Since 5 looks as if it might be maximal, let's check it (the reader may check the remaining cases, showing that none of the other numbers is maximal either). Is there no $y$ for which $y M 5$? Of course not, since 5 is a multiple of $5(5 \times 1 = 5)$. Thus, 5 cannot be maximal.

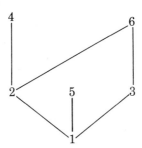

29. Since the set can be linearly ordered, we can evidently impose a preference relation on any of its subsets. But in Exercise 23 we have already shown that such a (sub)set must possess at least one maximal and one minimal element. Thus, it remains simply to show here that the set can not contain more than one maximal (minimal) element. It cannot, because if if did, such maximal (minimal) elements would be incomparable.

30.  $(a_1, b_1)$ and $(a_2, b_1)$     $(a_1, b_2)$ and $(a_2, b_1)$     $(a_1, b_3)$ and $(a_2, b_1)$
     $(a_1, b_1)$ and $(a_2, b_2)$     $(a_1, b_2)$ and $(a_2, b_2)$     $(a_1, b_3)$ and $(a_2, b_2)$
     $(a_1, b_1)$ and $(a_2, b_3)$     $(a_1, b_2)$ and $(a_2, b_3)$     $(a_1, b_3)$ and $(a_2, b_3)$
     $f_1(a_1) = f_1(a_2) = b_1$
     $f_2(a_1) = b_1;\ f_2(a_2) = b_2$
     $f_3(a_1) = b_1;\ f_3(a_2) = b_3$
     $f_4(a_1) = b_2;\ f_4(a_2) = b_1$
     $f_5(a_1) = f_5(a_2) = b_2$
     $f_6(a_1) = b_2;\ f_6(a_2) = b_3$
     etc.

31.  $f_1(b_1) = f_1(b_2) = f_1(b_3) = a_1$
     $f_2(b_1) = a_2;\ f_2(b_2) = f_2(b_3) = a_1$
     $f_3(b_1) = f_3(b_3) = a_1;\ f_2(b_2) = a_2$
     etc.

32.  (a) $D = R = S$. The inverse of $f$ is also a function; $f(2) = 8, f(4) = 64,$
     $f(-4) = -64, f(1) = 1, f(-1) = -1, f(0) = 0, f(-2) = -8, f^{-1}(-8) =$
     $2, f^{-1}(-8) = -2, f^{-1}(-4) = \sqrt[3]{-4}.$
     (b) $D = S$, but $R = Sp$, where $Sp$ is the set of all positive real numbers.
     The inverse of $f$ is not a function since, for example, $f^{-1}(16) = 2$ or
     $-2$—that is to say, 16 has *two* possible images under $f^{-1}$. $f(2) = 16,$
     $f(4) = 264 = f(-4), f(1) = f(-1) = 1, f(0) = 0, f(-2) = 16, f^{-1}(8) =$
     $\sqrt[4]{8}, f^{-1}(-8) = \sqrt[4]{-8}$ (thus the image of $-8$ under $f^{-1}$ does not exist
     if we confine ourselves to real numbers alone), $f^{-1}(16) = 2.$

33.  (a) The set of all real numbers greater than
     $-5$ $-4$ $-3$ $-2$ $-1$ $0$ $1$ $2$ $3$     $-5$.

     (b) The set of all real numbers less than 2.
     $-2$ $-1$ $0$ $1$ $2$ $3$

     (c) The set of all negative real numbers.
     $0$

     (d) The set of all positive real numbers.
     $0$

     (e) The set of all nonnegative real numbers
     $0$     (this includes 0 since 0 is obviously not
     a negative number).

     (f) The set of all real numbers excluding 0.
     $0$

     (g) $\{x \mid x > 0\} \cap \{x \mid x < 0\} = \mathfrak{E}$—that is, the sets are disjoint (have no
     elements in common).
     (h) $\{x \mid x \geqslant 0\} \cap \{x \mid x \leqslant 0\} = \{0\}$. This consists of the single point at 0.
     (i) All real numbers except those in
     $-2$ $-1$ $0$ $1$ $2$ $3$ $4$ $5$ $6$     $\{x \mid 2 < x < 4\}$.

34.

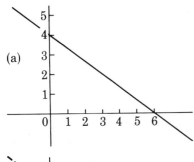

(a)

Notice that when you let $x = 0$ in the equation you get $y = 4$, so the graph cuts the $y$-axis at 4. Similarly, when $y = 0$, $x = 6$. The set consists of all points on the line.

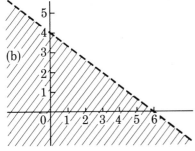

(b)

The sets consist of all points below the line $2x + 3y = 12$.

(c) The set consists of all points in the plane above the line $2x + 3y = 12$.

35.

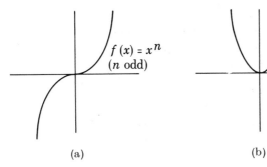

$f(x) = x^n$
($n$ odd)

$f(x) = x^n$
($n$ even)

(a)                    (b)

36. If $e'$ is also an identity element, then
$$e * e' = e' * e = e.$$
But since $e$, too, is an identity element,
$$e' * e = e * e' = e'.$$
Therefore,
$$e' = e.$$

37. We can write
$$i * (a * i') = i * e = i.$$

(Since $i'$ is the inverse of $a$, we know $a * i' = e$ by the definition of an inverse, and $i * e = i$ by the definition of an identity.)  We also have

$$(i * a) * i' = e * i' = i'.$$

(Because $i$ is the inverse of $a$, $i * a = e$ too.)  But since $*$ is associative,

$$(i * a) * i' = i * (a * i').$$

Therefore

$$i' = i.$$

38.  No element of $N$ has a multiplicative inverse except 1, which is its own inverse.

39.  (a) No, because the division of one integer by another does not always result in an integer (for example, $8 \div 2 = 4$ but $8 \div 3$ does not yield an *integer*).
(b) No, because the subtraction of a pair of natural numbers (or *positive* integers) does not always result in a natural number (that is, in a positive integer—for example, $5 - 8 = -3$).
(c) Yes (rational numbers include the positive and negative).
(d) Yes.

40.  (a) Yes (notice that $-I \times I = 1$, $(-I)(-I) = -1$, and so on).
(b) Yes. The inverse of 1 and $-1$ are, of course, 1 and $-1$. $I$ and $-I$ are inverse because $I(-I) = -I^2 = -(-1) = 1$.
(c) Yes (namely, 1).

# Chapter 5

1.  The phenomenon can not be represented by a digraph. For suppose $x \, R \, y$ and $y \, R \, x$ and that $R$ is also transitive. Then you could derive the result $x \, R \, x$, which violates the definition of a digraph.

2.  This requirement is *too strong*. It would confine our study exclusively to such highly redundant figures wherein every node is connected to every other. It is better to introduce such digraphs as special cases and call them *complete* digraphs. A complete digraph thus results whenever the under-lying relation, $R$, is connected (refer to the end of Section 4.4).

3.  No. Such a definition is *too strong*. The digraph in Figure 18 is evidently connected, but there are quite a number of node-pairs that do not belong to *any* diseg (for example, $n_8$ and $n_5$, $n_7$ and $n_5$, and so on).

4.  Unfortunately, this definition is *too weak*. Intuitively, the digraph below is not connected—it has two separate parts—and yet every node in it belongs to some diseg.

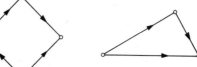

5. It is defined in Exercise 2. Alternatively, you might say something to the following effect: A digraph will be said to be *complete* whenever, for any $n_i$ and $n_j$ in $V$, either $(n_i, n_j) \in R$ or $(n_j, n_i) \in R$ (or, either $n_i \, R \, n_j$ or $n_j \, R \, n_i$); the "or" is, of course, the inclusive "or."

6. (a) Yes.
   (b) Yes, the middle graph.
   (c) No.
   (d) The first graph is an example of one that might be called *semistrongly connected*. Let us contrast it with the other two. The most obvious fact about the last graph is that it contains at least one pair of points neither of which is reachable from the other, namely, $1''$ and $5''$ (and there are others). This is not the case in the first graph. Nevertheless, the first graph is *not* strongly connected, for not *every* node is *reachable from* every other: thus, for example, while node 1 is reachable from node 4, node 4 is not reachable from node 1. In the case of the center figure all nodes are mutually reachable, though the path may sometimes be fairly circuitous: for example, we can get from $1'$ to $5'$ via 1245 (primes left off for ease in reading) but to reach $1'$ from $5'$ we must go through 53241. The problem now is to define the intermediate degree of connectedness exhibited by the first graph. One way to proceed is to say that a digraph is *semistrongly connected* if, for every $(x, y) \in D$, there exists a path $p(xy)$ or a path $p(yx)$ in $D$. The difference between this and a strongly connected digraph $D$ is that here, for every ordered pair of nodes $(x, y) \in D$, there exists at least one path $p(xy)$ in $D$—which says that any point is reachable from any other.

7. Let $D = (V, R)$ be a digraph. Then $D' = (V', R')$ is a subgraph of $D$ whenever $(n_i, n_j) \in R'$ if, and only if, $(n_i, n_j) \in R$ and $n_i$ and $n_j$ are elements of $V'$ (as well as being elements of $V$).

8. Yes. Intuitively, a subgraph is obtained whenever the nodes, and the disegs leading out of or into these nodes, are deleted from $V$. The simple digraph below proves the point for the subgraph not containing node 2:

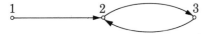

Notice, however, that if either node 1 or node 3 (and the appropriate disegs) is deleted, the remaining figure (subgraph) will be connected. Contrast this with the case below:

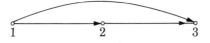

Here every subgraph obtained as a result of deleting any single node is connected.

9. $Dp = (V', R')$ is a *partial graph* of $D = (V, R)$ if $V' = V$ and $R' \subset R$. (Notice that $R'$ must be a *proper* subset of $R$.) The contrast between this notion and that of a subgraph may be brought out in terms of an example. When you go to an automobile club and they trace out a route for you to

follow between a pair of states on a highway map of the United States, they have given you a partial graph. If you request, say, a map of California, you will receive a subgraph of the graph of all U.S. highways. The major highways on this map of California constitute a partial subgraph of the original graph of U.S. roads and highways.

10.   There is only one:

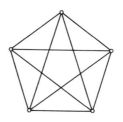

11.

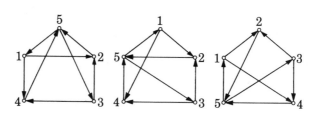

The single adjacency matrix below covers all three cases:

$$\begin{bmatrix} 0 & 1 & 0 & 1 & 0 \\ 0 & 0 & 0 & 0 & 1 \\ 0 & 1 & 0 & 1 & 0 \\ 0 & 0 & 0 & 0 & 1 \\ 1 & 0 & 1 & 0 & 0 \end{bmatrix}$$

12.   The digraphs are distinct (nonhomeomorphic). Two more distinct digraphs in this class are:

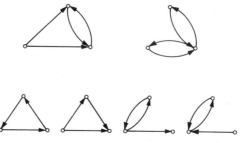

13.

14.  (a) $\begin{bmatrix} 3 \times 5 + 2 \times 3 & 3 \times 1 + 2 \times 2 \\ 5 \times 4 + 1 \times 3 & 4 \times 1 + 1 \times 2 \end{bmatrix} = \begin{bmatrix} 21 & 7 \\ 23 & 6 \end{bmatrix}$

   (b) $\begin{bmatrix} 2x_1 + 3x_2 - x_3 \\ x_1 - 2x_2 + x_3 \\ -x_1 - 3x_2 + x_3 \end{bmatrix}$

Note that the result is of the form

$$\begin{bmatrix} c_1 \\ c_2 \\ c_3 \end{bmatrix}$$

where

$$c_1 = 2x_1 + 3x_2 - x_3,$$
$$c_2 = x_1 - 2x_2 + x_3,$$
$$c_3 = -x_1 - 3x_2 + x_3.$$

There is nothing to prevent a matrix from consisting of just a single column (as above) or of just a single row. Ordinarily, such matrices are called column or row *vectors*.

(c) A square matrix with 1's along the main diagonal and 0's everywhere else is called, for obvious reasons, a *unit matrix*. It functions as a unity element with respect to matrix multiplication and is symbolized $I$; we have: $A \times I = I \times A = A$, for any matrix $A$.

(d) No.

(e) The matrix all of whose elements are zero; it is sometimes symbolized $\underline{0}$; we have: $A + \underline{0} = \underline{0} + A = A$, for any matrix $A$.

(f) $\begin{bmatrix} 0 & 0 \\ 0 & 0 \end{bmatrix}$

Notice the difference here from the case in ordinary algebra: it is possible for the product of two matrices to be zero even though neither factor is zero. That is, with matrices, we can have

$$X \cdot Y = \underline{0}$$

even though

$$X \neq \underline{0} \quad \text{and} \quad Y \neq \underline{0}.$$

In algebra, of course, $xy = 0$ means that either $x$ must be zero or $y$ must be zero (possibly both).

15. $AA^{-1} = A^{-1}A = I$ (see discussion under Exercise 14(c) above).

16. Premultiply (or postmultiply) both sides of the matrix equation by $A^{-1}$, where $A^{-1}$ is the inverse of $A$:

$$A^{-1}AX = A^{-1}B$$

or

$$IX = A^{-1}B$$

or

$$X = A^{-1}B.$$

The matrix equation has thus been solved for $X$. The problem is how to find $A^{-1}$, given any matrix $A$.

17. $X = A^{-1}$, provided that $A$ has an inverse, which may not be true—that is, the equation does *not* always have a solution. (See answers to Exercise 19.)

18. Multiplying together the two matrices on the left of the equality, we have

$$\begin{bmatrix} a + 2c & b + 2d \\ 3a + 4c & 3b + 4d \end{bmatrix} = \begin{bmatrix} 1 & 0 \\ 0 & 1 \end{bmatrix}.$$

Therefore,

$$a + 2c = 1,$$
$$b + 2d = 0,$$
$$3a + 4c = 0,$$
$$3b + 4d = 1.$$

(Recall that if two matrices are equal, they must be equal element for element.)

If we multiply the first equation through by 3 and subtract the third equation from it, we find

$$\begin{array}{ccc} 3a + 6c = 3 & \quad\text{or}\quad & c = \tfrac{3}{2}. \\ 3a + 4c = 0 & & \\ \hline \quad\; 2c = 3 & & \end{array}$$

Knowing $c$, we may substitute its value in the first equation to find

$$a + 3 = \; 1,$$
$$a = -2.$$

Similarly, multiplying the second equation through by 3 and subtracting the last equation,

$$\begin{array}{ccc} 3b + 6d = 0 & \quad\text{or}\quad & d = -\tfrac{1}{2}; \\ 3b + 4d = 1 & & \\ \hline \quad\; 2d = -1 & & \end{array}$$

then

$$b = 1.$$

So the inverse of

$$\begin{bmatrix} 1 & 2 \\ 3 & 4 \end{bmatrix}$$

must be

$$\begin{bmatrix} -2 & 1 \\ \tfrac{3}{2} & -\tfrac{1}{2} \end{bmatrix}.$$

As a check, notice that, indeed,

$$\begin{bmatrix} 1 & 2 \\ 3 & 4 \end{bmatrix} \times \begin{bmatrix} -2 & 1 \\ \tfrac{3}{2} & -\tfrac{1}{2} \end{bmatrix} = \begin{bmatrix} 1 & 0 \\ 0 & 1 \end{bmatrix}.$$

19. Proceeding in the same way as in the previous problem, we write

$$\begin{bmatrix} 3 & 2 \\ 6 & 4 \end{bmatrix} \begin{bmatrix} a & b \\ c & d \end{bmatrix} = \begin{bmatrix} 1 & 0 \\ 0 & 1 \end{bmatrix}.$$

Therefore

$$3a + 2c = 1,$$
$$3b + 2d = 0,$$
$$6a + 4c = 0,$$
$$6b + 4a = 1,$$

or, dividing the last two equations through by 2,

$$3a + 2c = 1,$$
$$3b + 2d = 0,$$
$$3a + 2c = 0,$$
$$3b + 2d = 1.$$

But there is something clearly wrong here. The first and third equations are clearly incompatible, as are the second and last equations—we have an inconsistent system of equations. Thus, the matrix

$$\begin{bmatrix} 3 & 2 \\ 6 & 4 \end{bmatrix}$$

does not have an inverse—that is, not every matrix has an inverse!

20.

$$A^2 = \begin{bmatrix} 1 & 3 \\ 2 & 4 \end{bmatrix} \times \begin{bmatrix} 1 & 3 \\ 2 & 4 \end{bmatrix} = \begin{bmatrix} 7 & 15 \\ 10 & 22 \end{bmatrix}.$$

21.   Yes. Obviously, $\begin{bmatrix} 1 & 0 \\ 0 & 1 \end{bmatrix}$ is a square root of $\begin{bmatrix} 1 & 0 \\ 0 & 1 \end{bmatrix}$, since

$$\begin{bmatrix} 1 & 0 \\ 0 & 1 \end{bmatrix} \times \begin{bmatrix} 1 & 0 \\ 0 & 1 \end{bmatrix} = \begin{bmatrix} 1 & 0 \\ 0 & 1 \end{bmatrix}.$$

But so are the following matrices:

$$\begin{bmatrix} 1 & 0 \\ 0 & -1 \end{bmatrix}, \quad \begin{bmatrix} -1 & 0 \\ 0 & 1 \end{bmatrix}, \quad \begin{bmatrix} -1 & 0 \\ 0 & -1 \end{bmatrix},$$

because

$$\begin{bmatrix} 1 & 0 \\ 0 & -1 \end{bmatrix}^2 = \begin{bmatrix} 1 & 0 \\ 0 & 1 \end{bmatrix}$$

and

$$\begin{bmatrix} -1 & 0 \\ 0 & 1 \end{bmatrix}^2 = \begin{bmatrix} 1 & 0 \\ 0 & 1 \end{bmatrix}$$

and so on. In fact,

$$\begin{bmatrix} 0 & x \\ 1/x & 0 \end{bmatrix}^2 = \begin{bmatrix} 1 & 0 \\ 0 & 1 \end{bmatrix},$$

where $x$ is any real number. Thus, the matrix $\begin{bmatrix} 1 & 0 \\ 0 & 1 \end{bmatrix}$ has an infinite number of square roots. Recall that in ordinary algebra every real number has only (in fact, exactly) two square roots; in particular, the square roots of unity are 1 and $-1$, since $(1)^2 = (-1)^2 = 1$.

22.   No. While it is true that you can go from

$$AB = AC$$

to

$$B = C$$

by, say, premultiplying the first equation through by $A^{-1}$, the fact remains that $A^{-1}$ does not always "exist" (that is, not every matrix has an inverse), so you can not always just "cancel" the $A$ appearing on both sides of the equation. Incidentally, you *never did* cancel, even in ordinary algebra, for to write

$$\not{a}b = \not{a}c$$

—that is, to cross out letters of the alphabet—is *not* to do mathematics. Drawing a line through a letter is not a *mathematical* operation, whatever else it may be. Mathematically, what you did was *divide* (a mathematical operation) both sides of the equation by $a$ and then used the fact that $a/a$ is (defined as) 1 and the fact that $1 \cdot b = b$ (and $1 \cdot c = c$). But, even in ordinary algebra, you cannot *in general* go from

$$ab = ac$$

to

$$b = c.$$

The exception occurs, as you may well recall, when $a = 0$. Another way of looking at it is that you can go from the first to the second equation by *multiplying* both sides by $a^{-1}$, the inverse of $a$, where $a^{-1} = 1/a$, noting that $a^{-1}$ does not exist when $a = 0$. The difference in the case of matrices is that $A^{-1}$ may fail to exist even when $A \neq 0$.

23.

$$\begin{vmatrix} 0 & 1 & 0 & 0 & 0 \\ 1 & 0 & 1 & 0 & 1 \\ 0 & 0 & 0 & 1 & 0 \\ 1 & 1 & 1 & 0 & 0 \\ 1 & 0 & 0 & 1 & 0 \end{vmatrix}$$

$$d_i(1) = 3, \quad d_i(2) = 2, \quad d_i(3) = 2, \quad d_i(4) = 2, \quad d_i(5) = 1;$$
$$d_o(1) = 1, \quad d_o(2) = 3, \quad d_o(3) = 1, \quad d_o(4) = 3, \quad d_o(5) = 2;$$
$$d(1) = 4, \quad d(2) = 5, \quad d(3) = 3, \quad d(4) = 5, \quad d(5) = 3;$$

Notice that the sum of the $d_i$ is equal to the sum of the $d_o$, which is equal to the total number of disegs, namely, 10. From the matrix it is obvious that the sums of the 1's across the rows must equal the sums of the 1's down the columns and that the sum of all the 1's in the matrix gives the total number of disegs.

24.

|   | a | b | c | d | e |
|---|---|---|---|---|---|
| a | 0 | 1 | 1 | 1 | 1 |
| b | 0 | 0 | 1 | 1 | 1 |
| c | 0 | 0 | 0 | 1 | 1 |
| d | 0 | 0 | 0 | 0 | 1 |
| e | 0 | 0 | 0 | 0 | 0 |

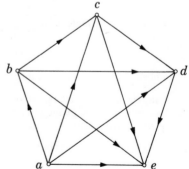

The digraph happens, in particular, to be an oriented graph. A typical situation giving rise to such an oriented graph would be one in which a number of entities (things or people) are ranked in order of increasing importance.

25.
$$M^2 = \begin{bmatrix} 0 & 1 & 1 & 1 & 1 \\ 0 & 0 & 1 & 1 & 1 \\ 0 & 0 & 0 & 1 & 1 \\ 0 & 0 & 0 & 0 & 1 \\ 0 & 0 & 0 & 0 & 0 \end{bmatrix} \times \begin{bmatrix} 0 & 1 & 1 & 1 & 1 \\ 0 & 0 & 1 & 1 & 1 \\ 0 & 0 & 0 & 1 & 1 \\ 0 & 0 & 0 & 0 & 1 \\ 0 & 0 & 0 & 0 & 0 \end{bmatrix} = \begin{bmatrix} 0 & 0 & 1 & 2 & 3 \\ 0 & 0 & 0 & 1 & 2 \\ 0 & 0 & 0 & 0 & 1 \\ 0 & 0 & 0 & 0 & 0 \\ 0 & 0 & 0 & 0 & 0 \end{bmatrix}.$$

Thus, for example, there is a 2-diseg-long path between nodes $a$ and $c$, two 2-diseg-long paths between $a$ and $d$, and three 2-diseg-long paths between nodes $a$ and $e$.

26.
$$M^3 = M^2 \times M = \begin{bmatrix} 0 & 0 & 1 & 2 & 3 \\ 0 & 0 & 0 & 1 & 2 \\ 0 & 0 & 0 & 0 & 1 \\ 0 & 0 & 0 & 0 & 0 \\ 0 & 0 & 0 & 0 & 0 \end{bmatrix} \begin{bmatrix} 0 & 1 & 1 & 1 & 1 \\ 0 & 0 & 1 & 1 & 1 \\ 0 & 0 & 0 & 1 & 1 \\ 0 & 0 & 0 & 0 & 1 \\ 0 & 0 & 0 & 0 & 0 \end{bmatrix} = \begin{bmatrix} 0 & 0 & 0 & 1 & 3 \\ 0 & 0 & 0 & 0 & 1 \\ 0 & 0 & 0 & 0 & 0 \\ 0 & 0 & 0 & 0 & 0 \\ 0 & 0 & 0 & 0 & 0 \end{bmatrix}.$$

This says that there are only five 3-diseg-long paths in the digraph: one between nodes $a$ and $d$, three between $a$ and $e$, and one between $b$ and $e$. (Check the figure.)

27. (a)
$$\begin{bmatrix} 0 & 0 & 0 & 0 & 0 \\ 1 & 0 & 0 & 0 & 1 \\ 0 & 1 & 0 & 1 & 0 \\ 0 & 1 & 0 & 0 & 1 \\ 0 & 0 & 1 & 0 & 0 \end{bmatrix} \otimes \begin{bmatrix} 0 & 1 & 0 & 0 & 0 \\ 0 & 0 & 1 & 0 & 1 \\ 1 & 0 & 0 & 1 & 1 \\ 0 & 0 & 1 & 0 & 1 \\ 1 & 0 & 0 & 1 & 0 \end{bmatrix} = \begin{bmatrix} 0 & 0 & 0 & 0 & 0 \\ 0 & 0 & 0 & 0 & 1 \\ 0 & 0 & 0 & 1 & 0 \\ 0 & 0 & 0 & 0 & 1 \\ 0 & 0 & 0 & 0 & 0 \end{bmatrix}$$

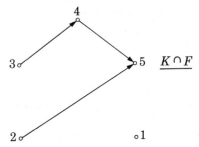

$K \cap F$

(b) Using Boolean addition of elements, we find
$$\begin{bmatrix} 0 & 0 & 0 & 0 & 0 \\ 1 & 0 & 0 & 0 & 1 \\ 0 & 1 & 0 & 1 & 0 \\ 0 & 1 & 0 & 0 & 1 \\ 0 & 0 & 1 & 0 & 0 \end{bmatrix} + \begin{bmatrix} 0 & 1 & 0 & 0 & 0 \\ 0 & 0 & 1 & 0 & 1 \\ 1 & 0 & 0 & 1 & 0 \\ 0 & 0 & 1 & 0 & 1 \\ 1 & 0 & 0 & 1 & 0 \end{bmatrix} = \begin{bmatrix} 0 & 1 & 0 & 0 & 0 \\ 1 & 0 & 1 & 0 & 1 \\ 1 & 1 & 0 & 1 & 0 \\ 0 & 1 & 1 & 0 & 1 \\ 1 & 0 & 1 & 1 & 0 \end{bmatrix}$$

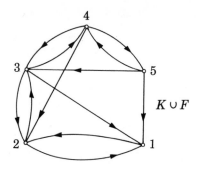

$K \cup F$

(c) Using modulo 2 addition:

$$\begin{bmatrix} 0 & 0 & 0 & 0 & 0 \\ 1 & 0 & 0 & 0 & 1 \\ 0 & 1 & 0 & 1 & 0 \\ 0 & 1 & 0 & 0 & 1 \\ 0 & 0 & 1 & 0 & 0 \end{bmatrix} + \begin{bmatrix} 0 & 1 & 0 & 0 & 0 \\ 0 & 0 & 1 & 0 & 1 \\ 1 & 0 & 0 & 1 & 0 \\ 0 & 0 & 1 & 0 & 1 \\ 1 & 0 & 0 & 1 & 0 \end{bmatrix} = \begin{bmatrix} 0 & 1 & 0 & 0 & 0 \\ 1 & 0 & 1 & 0 & 0 \\ 1 & 1 & 0 & 0 & 0 \\ 0 & 1 & 1 & 0 & 0 \\ 1 & 0 & 1 & 1 & 0 \end{bmatrix}$$

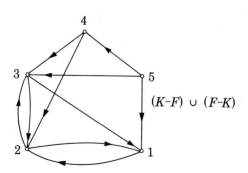

$(K\text{-}F) \cup (F\text{-}K)$

# Chapter 6

1. Proof that $p(E) + p(\overline{E}) = 1$: From set theory you know that for $E \subseteq \mathfrak{A}$,

$$E \cup \overline{E} = \mathfrak{A},$$

therefore

$$p(E \cup \overline{E}) = p(\mathfrak{A}).$$

But from axiom (iii)

$$p(E \cup \overline{E}) = p(E) + p(\overline{E}),$$

since $E$ and $\overline{E}$ are evidently mutually exclusive (since set theory tells us that $E \cap \overline{E} = \mathfrak{E}$ for any $E \subseteq \mathfrak{A}$. And from axiom (ii) $p(\mathfrak{A}) = 1$. Therefore

$$p(E) + p(\overline{E}) = 1.$$

(a) Now, suppose it were possible for $p(E)$ to be greater than 1; then $p(\bar{E})$ would have to be less than zero (that is, negative) for the sum to come out equal to 1. But this contradicts axiom (i). Thus, since the assumption that $p(E) > 1$ has led to a contradiction, the only remaining possibility is that $p(E) \leqslant 1$. Furthermore, owing to axiom (i) we have really established that

$$0 \leqslant p(E) \leqslant 1$$

for all $E \subseteq \mathfrak{A}$.

(b) $\bar{\mathfrak{A}} = \mathfrak{E}$; then $\mathfrak{A} \cup \mathfrak{A} = \mathfrak{A} \cup \mathfrak{E} = \mathfrak{A}$. From the result established under (a), $p(\mathfrak{E}) = 1 - p(\mathfrak{A})$, since $\bar{\mathfrak{E}} = \mathfrak{A}$. Therefore, $p(\mathfrak{E}) = 1 - 1 = 0$.

2. Whatever $p(E \cup \bar{E})$ may mean, no one would quarrel with the statement that

$$p(E \cup \bar{E}) = p(E \cup \bar{E}).$$

You have only to look at both sides of the equality to see this. But if you also know that

$$E \cup \bar{E} = \mathfrak{A},$$

then you may substitute $\mathfrak{A}$ for $E \cup \bar{E}$ where it appears in the parentheses on the right, getting

$$p(E \cup \bar{E}) = p(\mathfrak{A}).$$

3. $p(B - A) = p(B) - p(A)$. As you may recall from Chapter 4, any set $B$ may be thought of as the union of two mutually exclusive sets:

$$B = (A \cap B) \cup (\bar{A} \cap B).$$

But since $A \subseteq B$, we have $A \cap B = A$, so

$$B = A \cup (\bar{A} \cap B).$$

Therefore,

$$p(B) = p(A) + p(\bar{A} \cap B)$$

or

$$p(B) - p(A) = p(\bar{A} \cap B) = p(B - A)$$

since $B - A$ means $\bar{A} \cap B$.

4. Since $p(B) - p(A) = p(B - A)$ and since $p(B - A)$ can not be a negative number (it being a probability), we must have $p(B) \geqslant p(A)$.

5. Since $B = A \cup B$ and $A = A \cap B$ when $A \subseteq B$, and since also $p(B) \geqslant p(A)$ when $A \subseteq B$, therefore $p(A \cup B) \leq p(A \cap B)$.

6. $p(A \cup B \cup C) = p(A) + p(B \cup C) - p[A \cap (B \cup C)]$

$$= p(A) + p(B) + p(C) - p(B \cap C) - p[(A \cap B)$$

$$\cup (A \cap C)]$$

$$= p(A) + p(B) + p(C) - p(B \cap C) - p(A \cap B)$$

$$- p(A \cap C) + p[(A \cap B) \cap (A \cap C)]$$

$$= p(A) + p(B) + p(C) - p(AB) - p(AC) - p(BC)$$

$$+ p(ABC).$$

7. Since $m(A \cup B) = m(A) + m(B) - m(A \cap B)$, therefore $m(A \cap B) = m(A) + m(B) - m(A \cup B)$, from which we conclude that $m(A \cap B) \leqslant m(A) + m(B)$.

8. $p(A \cap B \cap C) = p(A \cap B)p(C \mid A \cap B) = p(A)p(B \mid A)p(C \mid AB)$.

9. Let $E_i$ be the event that the $i$th person draws his own name slip. The event whose probability is sought is $E_1 \cap E_2 \cap E_3$, and
$$p(E_1 \cap E_2 \cap E_3) = p(E_1)p(E_2 \mid E_1)p(E_3 \mid E_1E_2)$$
$$= \tfrac{1}{3} \times \tfrac{1}{2} \times 1 = \tfrac{1}{6}.$$

10. We have $p(R) = \tfrac{10}{100} = \tfrac{1}{10}$; $p(W) = \tfrac{40}{100} = \tfrac{2}{5}$; $p(B) = \tfrac{50}{100} = \tfrac{1}{2}$.
   (a) $p(\overline{W}) = 1 - p(W)$, so
   $$p(\overline{W} \cap \overline{W} \cap \overline{W}) = [1 - p(W)]^3 = (\tfrac{3}{5})^3 = \tfrac{27}{125}.$$
   (b) $p(W \cap W \cap W) = p(W) \cdot p(W) \cdot p(W) = (\tfrac{2}{5})^3 = \tfrac{8}{125}.$
   (c) $p(R \cap W \cap B) = p(R) \cdot p(W) \cdot p(B) = \tfrac{1}{10} \cdot \tfrac{2}{5} \cdot \tfrac{1}{2} = \tfrac{1}{50}.$
   (d) There are 6 permutations on the letters $RWB$—that is, any one of the events $RWB$, $RBW$, $WBR$, $WRB$, $BRW$, or $BWR$ is acceptable, each having a probability of $\tfrac{1}{50}$. Therefore, $p$ (one of each color will be drawn) $= 6(\tfrac{1}{50}) = \tfrac{3}{25}.$
   (e) The quickest way to find this is to subtract the probability that no $W$ occurs from 1. Thus,
   $$p(\text{at least one } W) = 1 - p(\overline{WWW}) = 1 - \tfrac{27}{125} = \tfrac{98}{125}.$$

11. (a) $p(\text{at least one } T) = 1 - p(\overline{T})$. The probability that no tail (that is, a head) will appear on the first toss is $\tfrac{1}{2}$; the same holds true on the second, third, ... , tenth toss. Therefore,
   $$p(\overline{T}) = (\tfrac{1}{2})^{10} = \tfrac{1}{1024}$$
   and
   $$p(\text{at least one } T) = 1 - \tfrac{1}{1024} = \tfrac{1023}{1024}.$$
   (b) Since the one tail may occur on the first toss, or on the second, ... , or on the tenth toss,
   $$p(\text{exactly one } T) = 10(\tfrac{1}{2})^{10} = \tfrac{10}{1024}.$$
   (c) This is the probability of getting either no T or one T; therefore;
   $$p(\text{at most one } T) = \tfrac{1}{1024} + \tfrac{10}{1024} = \tfrac{11}{1024}.$$

12. The divisors of 12 are 1, 2, 3, 4, 6, and 12, so the probability we seek is
   $$p(1 \cap 2 \cap 3 \cap 4 \cap 6 \cap 12) = p(1) + p(2) + p(3) + p(4) + p(6) + p(12)$$
   $$= 6 \times \tfrac{1}{12} = \tfrac{1}{2}.$$

13. The possible multiples of 3 that may be drawn are 3, 6, 9, and 12; the multiples of 4 are 4, 8, 12. The multiples of 3 or 4 are 3, 4, 6, 8, 9, and 12. Therefore,
   $$p(3 \cup 4 \cup 6 \cup 8 \cup 9 \cup 12) = \tfrac{1}{12} + \tfrac{1}{12} + \tfrac{1}{12} + \tfrac{1}{12} + \tfrac{1}{12} + \tfrac{1}{12} = \tfrac{6}{12} = \tfrac{1}{2}.$$
   Alternatively, let $p(T)$ = probability the number drawn is a multiple of 3 and $p(F)$ = probability it is a multiple of 4. The event whose probability is sought is $T \cup F$.
   $$p(T) = p(3) + p(6) + p(9) + p(12) = \tfrac{4}{12} = \tfrac{1}{3},$$
   $$p(F) = p(4) + p(8) + p(12) = \tfrac{3}{12} = \tfrac{1}{4},$$
   $$p(T \cap F) = p(12) = \tfrac{1}{12},$$

since 12 is the only number that is a multiple of both 3 and 4. Therefore,

$$p(T \cup F) = p(T) + p(F) - p(T \cap F)$$

$$= \tfrac{1}{3} + \tfrac{1}{4} - \tfrac{1}{12} = \tfrac{1}{2}$$

as before.

14. (a) Since half the cards in a deck are black, $p(B) = \tfrac{1}{2}$. Since a deck of 52 cards contains four Jacks, $p(J) = \tfrac{4}{52} = \tfrac{1}{13}$.

$$p(JB) = \tfrac{1}{13} \cdot \tfrac{1}{2} = \tfrac{1}{26},$$

$$p(J \cup B) = p(J) + p(B) - p(JB) = \tfrac{1}{2} + \tfrac{1}{13} - \tfrac{1}{26} = \tfrac{7}{13}.$$

(b) $p(R \cup S) = p(R) + p(S) = \tfrac{1}{2} + \tfrac{13}{52} = \tfrac{3}{4}$, since a card can not be both red and spade.

(c) $p(S \cup D) = p(S) + p(D) = \tfrac{1}{4} + \tfrac{1}{4} = \tfrac{1}{2}$.

15. Let $B_{rr}$ be the event that the box chosen is the one that contains two red marbles (that is, the event that the second marble is also red), and let $C_r$ be the event that the first marble chosen in the selected box is a red one. Then

$$p(B_{rr} \mid C_r) = \frac{p(C_r \mid B_{rr}) \cdot p(B_{rr})}{p(C_r)},$$

where

$$p(C_r) = p(C_r \mid B_{rr}) \cdot p(B_{rr}) + p(C_r \mid B_{br})p(B_{br}) + p(C_r \mid B_{bb})p(B_{bb})$$

$$= 1 \cdot \tfrac{1}{3} + \tfrac{1}{2} \cdot \tfrac{1}{3} + 0 \cdot \tfrac{1}{3} = \tfrac{1}{2}$$

so

$$p(B_{rr} \mid C_r) = \frac{1 \cdot \tfrac{1}{3}}{\tfrac{1}{2}} = \tfrac{2}{3}.$$

16. Let $C$ = passes course and $Q$ = passes qualifying test. Then $p(Q \mid C) = 0.70$, $p(Q \mid \overline{C}) = 0.20$, $p(C) = 0.50 = p(\overline{C})$, and

$$p(C \mid Q) = \frac{p(Q \mid C)p(C)}{p(Q)} = \frac{p(Q \mid C)p(C)}{p(Q \mid C)p(C) + p(Q \mid \overline{C})p(\overline{C})}$$

$$= \frac{0.70 \times 0.50}{0.70 \times 0.50 + 0.20 \times 0.50}$$

$$= \frac{0.35}{0.45} = \frac{7}{9} = 78\%.$$

This is the probability that a student will pass the course given that he has passed the test. Notice that this probability is considerably greater than the 50–50 chance of passing the course in general.

The probability that the department head is right is

$$p(C \cap Q) + p(\overline{C} \cap Q) = p(Q \mid C)p(C) + p(\overline{Q} \mid \overline{C})p(\overline{C})$$

$$= 0.70 \times 0.50 + 0.80 \times 0.50$$

$$= 0.75.$$

If he does not use the test, but admits everyone, his probability of being right that is, of having a student pass the course) is, of course, only 0.50.

17.  (a)  $B(4; 10, 0.3) = \dfrac{10!}{4!6!} (0.3)^4(0.7)^6$

$\qquad = \dfrac{7 \times 8 \times 9 \times 10}{4!} (0.09)(0.09)(0.49)(0.49)(0.49)$

$\qquad = 7 \times 3 \times 10 \times 0.008 \times 0.118 = 0.2.$

(b)  $B(4; 10, 0.3) + B(5; 10, 0.3) + B(6; 10, 0.3) + B(7; 10, 0.3) +$
 $B(8; 10, 0.3) + B(9; 10, 0.3) + B(10; 10, 0.3) = 1 - B(0; 10, 0.3) -$
 $B(1; 10, 0.3) - B(2; 10, 0.3) - B(3; 10, 0.3) - B(4; 10, 0.3),$
 since the probability of obtaining at least four successes is equal to one
 minus the probability of obtaining at most four successes.

(c)  $1 - q^n = 1 - (0.7)^{10} = 1 - 0.028 = 0.97$ (roughly).

18.  (a)  $G(1; 0.3) + G(2; 0.3) + G(3; 0.3) = (0.3)^0(0.1) + (0.3)(0.1) + (0.3)^2(0.1)$

$\qquad = 0.1 + 0.03 + 0.009$

$\qquad = 0.139.$

(b)  $= 1 - G(1; 0.3) - G(2; 0.3) = 1 - 0.1 - 0.03 = 0.87.$

19.  (a)  $P(10; 4, 0.3) = \dfrac{9!}{3! \, 6!} (0.3)^4(0.7)^6 = 7 \times 4 \times 3 \times 0.0081 \times 0.118$

$\qquad = 0.08.$

(b)  $P(8; 4, 0.3) = \dfrac{7!}{3! \, 4!} (0.3)^4(0.7)^4 = 5 \times 7 \times 0.00081 \times 0.24 = 0.068.$

(c)  0.7, the same as on any other trial.

# Index